Everyday
Mathematics®

The University of Chicago School Mathematics Project

Assessment Supplement

Grades **K-6**

Wright Group

The McGraw·Hill Companies

The University of Chicago School Mathematics Project (UCSMP)

Max Bell, Director, UCSMP Elementary Materials Component;
   Director, *Everyday Mathematics* First Edition
James McBride, Director, *Everyday Mathematics* Second Edition
Andy Isaacs, Director, *Everyday Mathematics* Third Edition
Amy Dillard, Associate Director, *Everyday Mathematics* Third Edition

Technical Art

Diana Barrie

Photo Credits

©Janis Christie/Getty Images, cover, *top left*; ©Getty Images, cover, *bottom right*;
Sharon Hoogstraten, cover, *bottom left*; ©Stephen Simpson/Getty Images, cover, *top right*.

www.WrightGroup.com

Printed in The United States of America.

Send all inquiries to:
Wright Group/McGraw-Hill
P.O. Box 812960
Chicago, IL 60681

ISBN 978-0-07-618778-2
MHID 0-07-618778-0

1 2 3 4 5 6 7 8 9 MAZ 12 11 10 09 08 07

The McGraw·Hill Companies

Contents

Introduction

This book contains the Beginning-of-Year, Mid-Year, and End-of-Year Assessments for Grades 1–6 and the three periodic assessments for Kindergarten. Answers for each written assessment as well as Individual Profiles of Progress and Class Checklists for assessing Kindergarten students are provided at the back of this book (see pages 168–211). The assessments in this book may be photocopied. The items on these assessments are linked to specific Grade-Level Goals, so teachers can monitor students' progress toward meeting those goals. For detailed information about how assessment problems in Grades 1–6 of the Beginning-of-Year, Mid-Year, and End-of-Year Assessments map to specific Grade-Level Goals, see pages 1–36 of this book.

The assessments in this book can serve as one part of a balanced assessment plan. They can be used to provide evidence of students' knowledge of important concepts and skills at key points in time during the school year. These assessments complement the ongoing and periodic assessments that appear within lessons and at the end of each unit. For more information about developing a balanced assessment plan, refer to the *Assessment Handbook*.

Beginning-of-Year Assessments (Grades 1–6)

For each grade, the Beginning-of-Year Assessment is an entry-level assessment that is a parallel form of the End-of-Year Assessment. These Beginning-of-Year Assessments can be used for two principal purposes. First, since they parallel the End-of-Year Assessments, these assessments can be used to establish baselines for measuring students' growth over the year, provided they are administered under the same conditions each time. Measuring such growth is an important aspect of summative assessment: It's important to know both whether students have reached the standards set for their grade and also what progress they have made over the course of the year.

Second, the Beginning-of-Year Assessments can provide valuable formative assessment information that teachers can use to tailor their instruction to fit their students' needs. In particular, the Beginning-of-Year Assessments can help teachers identify both students who have key knowledge and skills for a given grade level and may be on path to exceeding grade-level expectations and also students who need help with prerequisite knowledge and skills and may be in danger of falling behind. Note, however, that formative assessment opportunities occur throughout *Everyday Mathematics*, in Math Boxes and other daily work, in the end-of-unit Progress Checks, in the Informing Instruction notes in lessons, and so on. The Beginning-of-Year Assessments in this book are not the only tools for gathering data for formative assessment.

The Beginning-of-Year Assessments are not intended for summative assessment (beyond their role in establishing baselines for measuring growth). For this reason, the assessments have not been divided into Part A and Part B to distinguish between summative and formative questions. At the beginning of the school year, students are not expected to have the same level of knowledge and understanding of grade-level skills and concepts as they are expected to have at the end of the school year. The authors of *Everyday Mathematics* recommend using the Beginning-of-Year Assessments to establish baselines for measuring growth and to gather information about students' prior knowledge to help guide instruction, but not to assign grades.

As implied by the name, the Beginning-of-Year Assessment should be administered at the beginning of the school year. The Beginning-of-Year Assessments can also be administered to new or transfer students who join the class throughout the school year to help identify their specific needs with respect to Grade-Level Goals.

Mid-Year and End-of-Year Assessments (Grades 1–6)

The Mid-Year and End-of-Year Assessments each provide information that can be used for both summative and formative purposes. For Grades 1–6, each test has two parts, Part A and Part B. Part A provides summative information and may be used for grading purposes. Part B provides formative information that may be used for planning future instruction.

The Mid-Year Assessments are to be administered about halfway through the school year; for specific directions about timing, see the *Teacher's Lesson Guide*. The Mid-Year Assessments can also be administered to new or transfer students who join the class during the second half of the school year to help identify their specific needs related to Grade-Level Goals.

The End-of-Year Assessments are to be administered at the end of the school year. They provide a snapshot of students' progress towards meeting Grade-Level Goals. The End-of-Year Assessments are primarily summative in purpose, but also provide data that can be used to inform instruction over the summer or in the following grade.

These periodic assessments should be combined with other progress-monitoring assessments, such as the Recognizing Student Achievement tasks in each lesson and the Progress Check at the end of each unit, to create collections of assessment data that can provide valid and reliable evidence about students' progress toward mastering the Grade-Level Goals.

Kindergarten Periodic Assessments

The Baseline, Mid-Year, and End-of-Year Assessments serve the same general purposes in Kindergarten as they do in Grades 1–6, that is, they provide information about children's progress toward Grade-Level Goals at set points during the year. As in the other grades, this periodic assessment information can and should be used in conjunction with a range of ongoing assessment information as part of a balanced assessment plan. (See pages 8–13 and 35 in the Kindergarten *Assessment Handbook* for more information about ongoing assessment in Kindergarten and an overview of the key steps in assessment for *Kindergarten Everyday Mathematics*.)

Since Kindergarten students cannot fully or reliably show what they know through written assessment tasks, the Kindergarten periodic assessments involve low-key interactions with the teacher and hands-on tasks, such as working with manipulatives or playing games. Most of these periodic assessment tasks are best done with individual children or in small groups, but some can be integrated as part of whole-group activities. Many tasks can be set up in a center so a teacher can work with one or a few children at a time.

Pages 37–39 of the *Kindergarten Assessment Handbook* include a range of suggestions for administering the Kindergarten periodic assessments. These suggestions are aimed at helping children feel comfortable while doing the tasks, tailoring the assessments to meet individual needs and approaches, and maximizing the information teachers can learn from the assessments. Some of the suggestions also pertain to logistics, such as scheduling, collecting materials, and recording assessment information. Individual and class record-keeping sheets for the periodic assessments are on pages 168–179 of this book.

The Kindergarten Baseline assessment tasks should be administered during the first few weeks of school—as soon as most children have settled into the routines of the classroom and teachers are able to set aside time to work with children independently or in small groups. Administering the tasks may be spread over the course of a few weeks. Teachers can use these early assessment tasks to establish a baseline for measuring future growth and to plan and tailor instruction according to individual students' needs.

The Mid-Year and End-of-Year assessment tasks can be used formatively and summatively—to plan and tailor instruction, complete report cards, conduct parent-teacher conferences, and communicate with other teachers. The task descriptions include information to help teachers determine whether children are making adequate progress toward the Kindergarten Grade-Level Goals. The Mid-Year periodic assessment tasks should be done about halfway through the school year—toward the end of Section 4 and while working in Section 5 of the Kindergarten *Teacher's Guide to Activities*. The End-of-Year assessment tasks should be done toward the end of the school year, while working in Section 8 of the *Teacher's Guide to Activities*.

Methods of Assessment in Mathematics Curricula

A basic principle of assessment is that inferences based on multiple measures are more reliable than those based on single measures. In *Everyday Mathematics*, assessments are classified by the context in which they take place and by the source of the assessment data they yield.

The three principal contexts for gathering assessment data are ongoing classroom instruction, periodic assessment events, and external assessments. In each of these contexts, data can be gathered either from students' work products or through observation. Combinations of these assessment contexts and sources of data yield six broad varieties of assessment: ongoing product assessment, such as gathering data from a Math Box problem; ongoing observational assessment, such as watching children play a game; periodic product assessment, such as the written assessments at the end of each unit; and so on. (See pages 3–4 of the *Assessment Handbook* for further details about assessment contexts and sources of evidence.)

The instruments in this book for Grades 1–6 are periodic product assessments; those for Kindergarten are periodic observational assessments. As such, these assessments are one important tool for a balanced program of assessment, but in themselves they are not sufficient. The data from these instruments should be complemented by data from ongoing assessments, such as the Recognizing Student Achievement tasks in every lesson; from other periodic assessments, such as the end-of-unit written assessments; and, possibly, from external assessments such as standardized tests. Only with such a balanced approach can teachers accurately and reliably modify their instruction to meet their students' needs, monitor their students' progress, and judge whether their students have reached the standards that have been set for them.

Special Considerations in Mathematics Assessment

It may be entirely appropriate to adapt these instruments in various ways to better meet individual needs. For example, it may be appropriate to administer an assessment in several shorter periods rather than in a single sitting, or to read an assessment aloud to a student who has difficulty reading. Incorporating such adaptations may yield useful information that may be otherwise unobtainable. See the *Differentiation Handbook* for suggestions for making such adaptations.

However, if an instrument is to be used to make comparisons, then its use needs to be fair across the units (students, classes, schools, etc.) being compared. For example, if a Beginning-of-Year Assessment is given with a certain time limit, then the same limit should be observed when the corresponding End-of-Year Assessment is given. Special accommodations for certain students may be entirely appropriate so that assessments yield valid and reliable data, but such accommodations may also make it impossible to use those assessments to make comparisons across students or across time. For example, if a Beginning-of-Year Assessment is read aloud to a student then comparisons to the corresponding End-of-Year Assessment may be difficult unless it too is read aloud.

Assessments as Guideposts

The tools for assessment in *Everyday Mathematics* are designed to help teachers...

◆ direct their students' learning

◆ assess where students are

◆ monitor student progress along learning trajectories

◆ verify that students arrive at mastery

These are difficult tasks, but the tools provided in this book and throughout *Everyday Mathematics* can help. With these tools, teachers can gather information about where their students stand with respect to the Grade-Level Goals for their grade and determine whether students will be prepared for success in higher levels of mathematics. Teachers can use this information to keep their students on track.

Grade 1 Beginning-of-Year Assessment Goals

The Beginning-of-Year Assessment (pages 46–51) provides an additional opportunity that you may use as part of your balanced assessment plan. It covers many of the important concepts and skills presented in *First Grade Everyday Mathematics*. Since the Beginning-of-Year Assessment parallels the End-of-Year Assessment, it can be used to establish a baseline for measuring students' growth over the year. The Beginning-of-Year Assessment can provide valuable formative assessment information to help you tailor instruction to fit students' needs. The following tables provide goals for all the problems in the Beginning-of-Year Assessment.

Problem(s)	Description	Grade-Level Goal
1	Use drawings to model halves, thirds, and fourths as equal parts of a region.	Number and Numeration Goal 4
2	Compare whole numbers.	Number and Numeration Goal 7
2	Read, write, and explain expressions using the symbols <, >, = with cues.	Patterns, Functions, and Algebra Goal 2
3	Identify plane and solid figures including circles, squares, spheres, pyramids, cones, and cubes.	Geometry Goal 1
4	Demonstrate proficiency with +/–0, +/–1, doubles, and sum-equals-ten addition facts.	Operations and Computation Goal 1
4	Use mental arithmetic to solve problems involving the addition and subtraction of 1-digit whole numbers with 1- or 2-digit whole numbers.	Operations and Computation Goal 2
4	Apply the Commutative Property of Addition and the Additive Identity to basic addition fact problems.	Patterns, Functions, and Algebra Goal 3
5	Collect and organize data to create a bar graph.	Data and Chance Goal 1
5	Use graphs to answer simple questions and draw conclusions; find the maximum and minimum of a data set.	Data and Chance Goal 2
6	Identify shapes having line symmetry.	Geometry Goal 2
7	Describe events using basic probability terms.	Data and Chance Goal 3
8	Read temperatures on Fahrenheit thermometers to the nearest 10°.	Measurement and Reference Frames Goal 3
9	Measure length using standard measuring tools.	Measurement and Reference Frames Goal 1
10	Use manipulatives, drawings, tally marks, and numerical expressions involving addition and subtraction of 1- or 2-digit numbers to give equivalent names for whole numbers to 100.	Number and Numeration Goal 6
11	Show time to the nearest quarter-hour on an analog clock.	Measurement and Reference Frames Goal 4

Problem(s)	Description, *continued*	Grade-Level Goal
12	Calculate the values of combinations of coins.	Operations and Computation Goal 2
12	Know the values of pennies, nickels, dimes, and quarters; make exchanges between coins.	Measurement and Reference Frames Goal 2
13	Solve problems involving function machines and "What's My Rule?" tables.	Patterns, Functions, and Algebra Goal 1
14	Count collections of objects accurately and reliably.	Number and Numeration Goal 2
14	Write whole numbers up to 1,000; identify places in such numbers.	Number and Numeration Goal 3
15	Calculate and compare the values of combinations of coins.	Operations and Computation Goal 2
15	Know the values of pennies, nickels, dimes, quarters, and dollar bills.	Measurement and Reference Frames Goal 2
15	Solve problems involving the addition or subtraction of whole numbers.	Operations and Computation Goal 2
16	Use drawings to model halves as equal parts of a collection.	Number and Numeration Goal 4
17	Use number grids to solve problems involving the addition and subtraction of whole numbers.	Operations and Computation Goal 2
18	Use manipulatives, number grids, tally marks, and mental arithmetic to solve problems involving the addition and subtraction of 1-digit whole numbers with 1- or 2-digit whole numbers.	Operations and Computation Goal 2
18	Extend numeric patterns.	Patterns, Functions, and Algebra Goal 1
19	Use manipulatives, number grids, tally marks, and mental arithmetic to solve problems involving the addition and subtraction of 2-digit whole numbers with 2-digit whole numbers.	Operations and Computation Goal 2
19	Identify parts-and-total situations.	Operations and Computation Goal 4
19	Write and explain number sentences using the symbols +, −, and =.	Patterns, functions, and Algebra Goal 2
20	Tell time to the nearest 5 minutes on an analog clock.	Measurement and Reference Frames Goal 4

Grade 1 Mid-Year Assessment Goals

The Mid-Year Assessment (pages 52–55) provides an additional opportunity that you may use as part of your balanced assessment plan. It covers some of the important concepts and skills presented in *First Grade Everyday Mathematics*. It should be used to complement the ongoing and periodic assessments that appear within lessons and at the end of units. The following tables provide the goals for all the problems in Part A and Part B of the Mid-Year Assessment.

Part A Recognizing Student Achievement

Problems 1–8 provide summative information and may be used for grading purposes.

Problem(s)	Description	Grade-Level Goal
1, 7	Count collections of objects accurately and reliably.	Number and Numeration Goal 2
1	Identify even and odd numbers.	Number and Numeration Goal 5
2	Write whole numbers up to 1,000.	Number and Numeration Goal 3
2	Order whole numbers.	Number and Numeration Goal 7
3	Count by 2s and 10s.	Number and Numeration Goal 1
4	Extend visual patterns.	Patterns, Functions, and Algebra Goal 1
5	Show time to the nearest hour and half-hour on an analog clock.	Measurement and Reference Frames Goal 4
6	Measure length using standard measuring tools.	Measurement and Reference Frames Goal 1
7	Use tally marks to give equivalent names for whole numbers.	Number and Numeration Goal 6
7, 8	Use tally marks to solve problems involving addition and subtraction of 1-digit whole numbers with 1- or 2-digit whole numbers; calculate the values of combinations of coins.	Operations and Computation Goal 2
7	Identify comparison situations.	Operations and Computation Goal 4
7	Organize data to create tally charts.	Data and Chance Goal 1
7	Use tally charts to answer simple questions.	Data and Chance Goal 2
8	Know the values of pennies, nickels, and dimes.	Measurement and Reference Frames Goal 2

Part B Informing Instruction

Problems 9–12 provide formative information that can be useful in planning future instruction.

Problem(s)	Description	Grade-Level Goal
9	Demonstrate proficiency with +0, +1, doubles, and sum-equals-ten addition facts.	Operations and Computation Goal 1
10	Count back by 5s.	Number and Numeration Goal 1
10	Solve problems involving the addition and subtraction of 1-digit whole numbers with 1- or 2-digit whole numbers.	Operations and Computation Goal 2
10	Solve problems involving Frames-and-Arrows diagrams.	Patterns, Functions, and Algebra Goal 1
11	Solve problems involving the addition and subtraction of 1-digit whole numbers with 1- or 2-digit whole numbers.	Operations and Computation Goal 2
11	Identify change-to-less, change-to-more, and parts-and-totals situations.	Operations and Computation Goal 4
11	Write and explain number sentences using the symbols +, −, and =; solve equations involving addition and subtraction.	Patterns, Functions, and Algebra Goal 2
12	Calculate the values of combinations of coins.	Operations and Computation Goal 2
12	Know the values of pennies, nickels, and dimes; make exchanges between coins.	Measurement and Reference Frames Goal 2

Grade 1 End-of-Year Assessment Goals

The End-of-Year Assessment (pages 56–61) provides an additional opportunity that you may use as part of your balanced assessment plan. It covers many of the important concepts and skills presented in *First Grade Everyday Mathematics*. It should be used to complement the ongoing and periodic assessments that appear within lessons and at the end of units. The following tables provide goals for all the problems in Part A and Part B of the End-of-Year Assessment.

Part A Recognizing Student Achievement

Problems 1–14 provide summative information and may be used for grading purposes.

Problem(s)	Description	Grade-Level Goal
1	Use drawings to model halves, thirds, and fourths as equal parts of a region.	Number and Numeration Goal 4
2	Compare whole numbers.	Number and Numeration Goal 7
2	Read, write, and explain expressions using the symbols <, >, = with cues.	Patterns, Functions, and Algebra Goal 2
3	Identify plane and solid figures including circles, squares, spheres, pyramids, cones, and cubes.	Geometry Goal 1
4	Demonstrate proficiency with +/−0, +/−1, doubles, and sum-equals-ten addition facts.	Operations and Computation Goal 1
4	Use mental arithmetic to solve problems involving the addition and subtraction of 1-digit whole numbers with 1- or 2-digit whole numbers.	Operations and Computation Goal 2
4	Apply the Commutative Property of Addition and the Additive Identity to basic addition fact problems.	Patterns, Functions, and Algebra Goal 3
5	Collect and organize data to create a bar graph.	Data and Chance Goal 1
5	Use graphs to answer simple questions and draw conclusions; find the maximum and minimum of a data set.	Data and Chance Goal 2
6	Identify shapes having line symmetry.	Geometry Goal 2
7	Describe events using basic probability terms.	Data and Chance Goal 3
8	Read temperatures on Fahrenheit thermometers to the nearest 10°.	Measurement and Reference Frames Goal 3
9	Measure length using standard measuring tools.	Measurement and Reference Frames Goal 1
10	Use manipulatives, drawings, tally marks, and numerical expressions involving addition and subtraction of 1- or 2-digit numbers to give equivalent names for whole numbers to 100.	Number and Numeration Goal 6
11	Show time to the nearest quarter-hour on an analog clock.	Measurement and Reference Frames Goal 4

Problem(s)	Description *continued*	Grade-Level Goal
12	Calculate the values of combinations of coins.	Operations and Computation Goal 2
12	Know the values of pennies, nickels, dimes, and quarters; make exchanges between coins.	Measurement and Reference Frames Goal 2
13	Solve problems involving function machines and "What's My Rule?" tables.	Patterns, Functions, and Algebra Goal 1
14	Count collections of objects accurately and reliably.	Number and Numeration Goal 2
14	Write whole numbers up to 1,000; identify places in such numbers.	Number and Numeration Goal 3

Part B Informing Instruction

Problems 15–20 provide formative information.

Problem(s)	Description	Grade-Level Goal
15	Calculate and compare the values of combinations of coins.	Operations and Computation Goal 2
15	Know the values of pennies, nickels, dimes, quarters, and dollar bills.	Measurement and Reference Frames Goal 2
15	Solve problems involving the addition or subtraction of whole numbers.	Operations and Computation Goal 2
16	Use drawings to model halves as equal parts of a collection.	Number and Numeration Goal 4
17	Use number grids to solve problems involving the addition and subtraction of whole numbers.	Operations and Computation Goal 2
18	Use manipulatives, number grids, tally marks, and mental arithmetic to solve problems involving the addition and subtraction of 1-digit whole numbers with 1- or 2-digit whole numbers.	Operations and Computation Goal 2
18	Extend numeric patterns.	Patterns, Functions, and Algebra Goal 1
19	Use manipulatives, number grids, tally marks, and mental arithmetic to solve problems involving the addition and subtraction of 2-digit whole numbers with 2-digit whole numbers.	Operations and Computation Goal 2
19	Identify parts-and-total situations.	Operations and Computation Goal 4
19	Write and explain number sentences using the symbols +, −, and =.	Patterns, Functions, and Algebra Goal 2
20	Tell time to the nearest 5 minutes on an analog clock.	Measurement and Reference Frames Goal 4

Grade 2 Beginning-of-Year Assessment Goals

The Beginning-of-Year Assessment (pages 62–67) provides an additional assessment opportunity that you may use as part of your balanced assessment plan. It covers many of the important concepts and skills presented in *Second Grade Everyday Mathematics.* Since the Beginning-of-Year Assessment parallels the End-of-Year Assessment, it can be used to establish a baseline for measuring students' growth over the year. The Beginning-of-Year Assessment can provide valuable formative assessment information to help teachers tailor instruction to fit their students' needs. The following tables provide goals for all the problems in the Beginning-of-Year Assessment.

Problem(s)	Description	Grade-Level Goal
1	Measure to the nearest inch and centimeter.	Measurement and Reference Frames Goal 1
2	Create a bar graph.	Data and Chance Goal 1
2a, 2b, 2c, 2d	Find the maximum, minimum, median, and mode.	Data and Chance Goal 2
3, 4	Model fractions as equal parts of a region and collection.	Number and Numeration Goal 3
5	Use drawings to model equivalent names for $\frac{1}{2}$.	Number and Numeration Goal 6
6a, 6b	Make reasonable estimates.	Operations and Computation Goal 3
7	Find the area.	Measurement and Reference Frames Goal 2
8a, 8b	Use manipulatives to solve 2-digit whole numbers addition.	Operations and Computation Goal 2
8c, 8d	Use manipulatives to solve 2-digit whole numbers subtraction.	Operations and Computation Goal 2
9a, 9b, 9c	Write the time to the nearest 5 minutes.	Measurement and Reference Frames Goal 6
10	Describe relationships between days in a week and hours in a day.	Measurement and Reference Frames Goal 3
11a, 11b	Use equal sharing and equal grouping.	Operations and Computation Goal 4
12a, 12b	Use counters to model multiplication.	Operations and Computation Goal 4
13a, 13b, 13c, 13d, 13e, 13f	Use =, +, and −.	Patterns, Functions, and Algebra Goal 2

Problem(s)	Description *continued*	Grade-Level Goal
14a	Calculate money amounts.	Operations and Computation Goal 2
14b	Write and solve number sentences using +, −, and =.	Patterns, Functions, and Algebra Goal 2
15	Make change.	Operations and Computation Goal 2
16	Write the fact family.	Operations and Computation Goal 4
17	Solve multiplication facts.	Operations and Computation Goal 4
18a, 18b	Use manipulatives to model fractions as equal parts of a region.	Number and Numeration Goal 3
19	Make change.	Operations and Computation Goal 2
20a, 20b	Solve 2- and 3-digit addition problems.	Operations and Computation Goal 2
20c, 20d, 20e	Solve 2- and 3-digit subtraction problems.	Operations and Computation Goal 2
21	Find the area.	Measurement and Reference Frames Goal 2
22	Identify the place and value of digits.	Number and Numeration Goal 2

Grade 2 Mid-Year Assessment Goals

The Mid-Year Assessment (pages 68–71) provides an additional assessment opportunity that you may use as part of your balanced assessment plan. This assessment covers some of the important concepts and skills presented in *Second Grade Everyday Mathematics*. It should be used to complement the ongoing and periodic assessments that appear within lessons and at the end of units. The following tables provide goals for all the problems in Part A and Part B of the Mid-Year Assessment.

Part A Recognizing Student Achievement

Problems 1–11 provide summative information and may be used for grading purposes.

Problem(s)	Description	Grade-Level Goal
1	Draw a line segment.	Geometry Goal 1
2	Find parallel lines.	Geometry Goal 1
3	Read the temperature.	Measurement and Reference Frames Goal 5
4	Write the fact family.	Operations and Computation Goal 1
5	Use the >, <, and = symbols.	Patterns, Functions, and Algebra Goal 2
6	Complete the number-grid piece.	Patterns, Functions, and Algebra Goal 1
7	Identify 2-dimensional shapes.	Geometry Goal 2
8	Identify 3-dimensional shapes.	Geometry Goal 2
9	Draw the time.	Measurement and Reference Frames Goal 6
10a	Solve parts-and-total situations.	Operations and Computation Goal 4
10b	Write the number model.	Patterns, Functions, and Algebra Goal 2
10c	Identify odd or even.	Number and Numeration Goal 4
11	Equivalent names for money.	Number and Numeration Goal 5

Part B Informing Instruction

Problems 12–16 provide formative information that can be useful in planning future instruction.

Problem(s)	Description	Grade-Level Goal
12	Fill in the Frames.	Patterns, Functions, and Algebra Goal 1
13a, 13b	Solve 2-digit addition.	Operations and Computation Goal 2
13c, 13d	Solve 2-digit subtraction.	Operations and Computation Goal 2
14	Draw an array to model multiplication.	Operations and Computation Goal 4
15	Find the rule and complete the table.	Patterns, Functions, and Algebra Goal 1
16	Make exchanges between coins and bills.	Measurement and Reference Frames Goal 4

Grade 2 End-of-Year Assessment Goals

The End-of-Year Assessment (pages 72–77) provides an additional opportunity that you may use as part of your balanced assessment plan. It covers many of the important concepts and skills presented in *Second Grade Everyday Mathematics*. It should be used to complement the ongoing and periodic assessments that appear within lessons and at the end of units. The following tables provide goals for all the problems in Part A and Part B of the End-of-Year Assessment.

Part A Recognizing Student Achievement

Problems 1–15 provide summative information and may be used for grading purposes.

Problem(s)	Description	Grade-Level Goal
1	Measure to the nearest inch and centimeter.	Measurement and Reference Frames Goal 1
2	Create a bar graph.	Data and Chance Goal 1
2a, 2b, 2c, 2d	Find the maximum, minimum, median, and mode.	Data and Chance Goal 2
3, 4	Model fractions as equal parts of a region and collection.	Number and Numeration Goal 3
5	Use drawings to model equivalent names for $\frac{1}{2}$.	Number and Numeration Goal 6
6a, 6b	Make reasonable estimates.	Operations and Computation Goal 3
7	Find the area.	Measurement and Reference Frames Goal 2
8a, 8b	Use manipulatives to solve 2-digit whole numbers addition.	Operations and Computation Goal 2
8c, 8d	Use manipulatives to solve 2-digit whole numbers subtraction.	Operations and Computation Goal 2
9a, 9b, 9c	Write the time to the nearest 5 minutes.	Measurement and Reference Frames Goal 6
10	Describe relationships between days in a week and hours in a day.	Measurement and Reference Frames Goal 3
11a, 11b	Use equal sharing and equal grouping.	Operations and Computation Goal 4
12a, 12b	Use counters to model multiplication.	Operations and Computation Goal 4
13a, 13b, 13c, 13d, 13e, 13f	Use =, +, and −.	Patterns, Functions, and Algebra Goal 2

Problem(s)	Description *continued*	Grade-Level Goal
14a	Calculate money amounts.	Operations and Computation Goal 2
14b	Write and solve number sentences using +, −, and =.	Patterns, Functions, and Algebra Goal 2
15	Make change.	Operations and Computation Goal 2

Part B Informing Instruction

Problems 16–22 provide formative information that can be useful in planning future instruction.

Problem(s)	Description	Grade-Level Goal
16	Write the fact family.	Operations and Computation Goal 4
17	Solve multiplication facts.	Operations and Computation Goal 4
18a, 18b	Use manipulatives to model fractions as equal parts of a region.	Number and Numeration Goal 3
19	Make change.	Operations and Computation Goal 2
20a, 20b	Solve 2- and 3-digit addition problems.	Operations and Computation Goal 2
20c, 20d, 20e	Solve 2- and 3-digit subtraction problems.	Operations and Computation Goal 2
21	Find the area.	Measurement and Reference Frames Goal 2
22	Identify the place and value of digits.	Number and Numeration Goal 2

Grade 3 Beginning-of-Year Assessment Goals

The Beginning-of-Year Assessment (pages 78–85) provides an additional opportunity that you may use as part of your balanced assessment plan. It covers many of the important concepts and skills presented in *Third Grade Everyday Mathematics*. Since the Beginning-of-Year Assessment parallels the End-of-Year Assessment, it can be used to establish a baseline for measuring students' growth over the year. The Beginning-of-Year Assessment can provide valuable formative assessment information to help you tailor instruction to fit students' needs.. The following tables provide the goals for all the problems in the Beginning-of-Year Assessment.

Problem(s)	Description	Grade-Level Goal
1a, b	Complete Frames-and-Arrows problems.	Patterns, Functions, and Algebra Goal 1
2a–c	Find the perimeter and area of a figure. Explain how the area was found.	Measurement and Reference Frames Goal 2
3	Solve a problem involving the addition and subtraction of decimals in a money context.	Operations and Computation Goal 2
3b, 8b, 20b	Write a number sentence to model a number story.	Patterns, Functions, and Algebra Goal 2
4a, 5a, 6a, 7a	Make reasonable estimates for whole number addition and subtraction problems.	Operations and Computation Goal 5
4b, 5b, 6b, 7b	Solve problems involving the addition and subtraction of whole numbers.	Operations and Computation Goal 2
8a	Explain strategy used to estimate an answer to a problem involving addition and subtraction.	Operations and Computation Goal 5
9a–c	Show and write time to the nearest minute on an analog clock.	Measurement and Reference Frames Goal 4
10	Identify a right angle.	Geometry Goal 1
11, 12a–d	Identify and describe plane and solid figures.	Geometry Goal 2
13, 14	Solve problems involving fractional parts of a collection.	Number and Numeration Goal 2
15a, b	Measure to the nearest $\frac{1}{2}$ inch and $\frac{1}{2}$ centimeter.	Measurement and Reference Frames Goal 1
16a–c	Write and model fractions.	Number and Numeration Goal 2
17	Use given data to complete a bar graph.	Data and Chance Goal 1
18a–d	Find the maximum, minimum, range, and median of a data set.	Data and Chance Goal 2

Problem(s)	Description, *continued*	Grade-Level Goal
19a, b	Use arrays, mental arithmetic, and paper-and-pencil algorithms to solve problems involving the multiplication of 2- and 3-digit whole numbers by 1-digit whole numbers.	Operations and Computation Goal 4
20a	Use repeated addition, arrays, and skip counting to model multiplication.	Operations and Computation Goal 6
21a–c	Describe rules for patterns and use them to solve problems.	Patterns, Functions, and Algebra Goal 1
22	Use mental arithmetic to solve problems involving the multiplication of multidigit numbers.	Operations and Computation Goal 4
23	Write number sentences using symbols $\times$, $\div$, and $=$.	Patterns, Functions, and Algebra Goal 2
24	Measure length.	Measurement and Reference Frames Goal 1
25	Solve problems involving fractional parts of a region.	Number and Numeration Goal 2
26a–d	Understand that grouping symbols can be used to affect the order in which operations are carried out.	Patterns, Functions, and Algebra Goal 3
27a	Use equal sharing and equal grouping to model division.	Operations and Computation Goal 6
27b	Write a number sentence to model a number story.	Patterns, Functions, and Algebra Goal 2
28a, b	Use arrays, mental arithmetic, and paper-and-pencil algorithms to solve problems involving the multiplication of multidigit whole numbers.	Operations and Computation Goal 4

Grade 3 Mid-Year Assessment Goals

The Mid-Year Assessment (pages 86–89) provides an additional opportunity that you may use as part of your balanced assessment plan. It covers some of the important concepts and skills presented in *Third Grade Everyday Mathematics*. It should be used to complement the ongoing and periodic assessments that appear within lessons and at the end of units. The following tables provide the goals for all the problems in Part A and Part B of the Mid-Year Assessment.

Part A Recognizing Student Achievement

Problems 1–13 provide summative information and may be used for grading purposes.

Problem(s)	Description	Grade-Level Goal
1a	Tell time on an analog clock.	Measurement and Reference Frames Goal 4
1b	Describe relationship between minutes in an hour.	Measurement and Reference Frames Goal 3
2a, b	Make reasonable estimates for whole number addition and subtraction problems.	Operations and Computation Goal 5
3a	Recognize and solve parts-and-total situations.	Operations and Computation Goal 6
4a, 5a	Solve number stories involving the addition and subtraction of whole numbers and decimals in a money context.	Operations and Computation Goal 2
3b, 4b, 5b	Write number sentences to model number stories.	Patterns, Functions, and Algebra Goal 2
6a, 7a	Use repeated addition, arrays, and skip counting to model multiplication; use equal sharing to model division.	Operations and Computation Goal 6
6b, 7b	Write number sentences to model number stories.	Patterns, Functions, and Algebra Goal 2
8a–f	Demonstrate automaticity with addition and subtraction facts.	Operations and Computation Goal 1
9a–f	Use the symbols >, <, and = to complete number sentences.	Patterns, Functions, and Algebra Goal 2
10	Identify places in decimals.	Number and Numeration Goal 1
11	Use given digits to write the smallest 6-digit number.	Number and Numeration Goal 6
12a, b	Solve problems involving addition and subtraction of whole numbers.	Operations and Computation Goal 2
13a, b	Solve Frames-and-Arrows puzzles involving multiples of 2 and 5.	Number and Numeration Goal 3

Part B Informing Instruction

Problems 14–18 provide formative information that can be used in planning future instruction.

Problem(s)	Description	Grade-Level Goal
14a	Draw lines of symmetry.	Geometry Goal 3
14b	Identify a pentagon.	Geometry Goal 2
15a	Recognize and describe a comparison situation.	Operations and Computation Goal 6
15b	Write a number sentence to model a number story.	Patterns, Functions, and Algebra Goal 2
16a, b	Solve problems involving the addition and subtraction of whole numbers.	Operations and Computation Goal 2
17	Describe events using basic probability terms.	Data and Chance Goal 3
18	Complete a "What's My Rule?" problem.	Patterns, Function, and Algebra Goal 1

Grade 3 End-of-Year Assessment Goals

The End-of-Year Assessment (pages 90–97) provides an additional opportunity that you may use as part of your balanced assessment plan. It covers many of the important concepts and skills presented in *Third Grade Everyday Mathematics*. It should be used to complement the ongoing and periodic assessments that appear within lessons and at the end of units. The following tables provide the goals for all the problems in Part A and Part B of the End-of-Year Assessment.

Part A Recognizing Student Achievement

Problems 1–21 provide summative information and may be used for grading purposes.

Problem(s)	Description	Grade-Level Goal
1a, b	Complete Frames-and-Arrows problems.	Patterns, Functions, and Algebra Goal 1
2a–c	Find the perimeter and area of a figure. Explain how the area was found.	Measurement and Reference Frames Goal 2
3	Solve a problem involving the addition and subtraction of decimals in a money context.	Operations and Computation Goal 2
3b, 8b, 20b	Write a number sentence to model a number story.	Patterns, Functions, and Algebra Goal 2
4a, 5a, 6a, 7a	Make reasonable estimates for whole number addition and subtraction problems.	Operations and Computation Goal 5
4b, 5b, 6b, 7b	Solve problems involving the addition and subtraction of whole numbers.	Operations and Computation Goal 2
8a	Explain strategy used to estimate an answer to a problem involving addition and subtraction.	Operations and Computation Goal 5
9a–c	Show and write time to the nearest minute on an analog clock.	Measurement and Reference Frames Goal 4
10	Identify a right angle.	Geometry Goal 1
11, 12a–d	Identify and describe plane and solid figures.	Geometry Goal 2
13, 14	Solve problems involving fractional parts of a collection.	Number and Numeration Goal 2
15a, b	Measure to the nearest $\frac{1}{2}$ inch and $\frac{1}{2}$ centimeter.	Measurement and Reference Frames Goal 1
16a–c	Write and model fractions.	Number and Numeration Goal 2
17	Use given data to complete a bar graph.	Data and Chance Goal 1
18a–d	Find the maximum, minimum, range, and median of a data set.	Data and Chance Goal 2

Problem(s)	Description, *continued*	Grade-Level Goal
19a, b	Use arrays, mental arithmetic, and paper-and-pencil algorithms to solve problems involving the multiplication of 2- and 3-digit whole numbers by 1-digit whole numbers.	Operations and Computation Goal 4
20a	Use repeated addition, arrays, and skip counting to model multiplication.	Operations and Computation Goal 6
21a–c	Describe rules for patterns and use them to solve problems.	Patterns, Functions, and Algebra Goal 1

Part B Informing Instruction

Problems 22–28 provide formative information.

Problem(s)	Description	Grade-Level Goal
22	Use mental arithmetic to solve problems involving the multiplication of multidigit numbers.	Operations and Computation Goal 4
23	Write number sentences using symbols ×, ÷ and =.	Patterns, Functions, and Algebra Goal 2
24	Measure length.	Measurement and Reference Frames Goal 1
25	Solve problems involving fractional parts of a region.	Number and Numeration Goal 2
26a–d	Understand that grouping symbols can be used to affect the order in which operations are carried out.	Patterns, Functions, and Algebra Goal 3
27a	Use equal sharing and equal grouping to model division.	Operations and Computation Goal 6
27b	Write a number sentence to model a number story.	Patterns, Functions, and Algebra Goal 2
28a, b	Use arrays, mental arithmetic, and paper-and-pencil algorithms to solve problems involving the multiplication of multidigit whole numbers.	Operations and Computation Goal 4

Grade 4 Beginning-of-Year Assessment Goals

The Beginning-of-Year Assessment (pages 98–105) provides an additional opportunity that you may use as part of your balanced assessment plan. It covers many of the important concepts and skills presented in *Fourth Grade Everyday Mathematics*. Since the Beginning-of-Year Assessment parallels the End-of-Year Assessment, it can be used to establish a baseline for measuring students' growth over the year. The Beginning-of-Year Assessment can provide valuable formative assessment information to help you tailor instruction to fit students' needs. The following tables provide the goals for all the problems in the Beginning-of-Year Assessment.

Problem(s)	Description	Grade-Level Goal
1	Solve problems involving fractional parts of a collection.	Number and Numeration Goal 2
2	Find multiples.	Number and Numeration Goal 3
3	Find factors.	Number and Numeration Goal 3
4	Rename fractions as decimals and percents.	Number and Numeration Goal 5
5	Compare fractions.	Number and Numeration Goal 6
6	Order fractions.	Number and Numeration Goal 6
7a, 7b	Multiply a multidigit whole number by a 2-digit whole number.	Operations and Computation Goal 4
7c, 7d	Divide a multidigit whole number by 1-digit whole number.	Operations and Computation Goal 4
8a, 8b	Add fractions.	Operations and Computation Goal 5
8c, 8d	Subtract fractions.	Operations and Computation Goal 5
9	Use given data to create a line graph.	Data and Chance Goal 1
10	Describe events using basic probability terms.	Data and Chance Goal 3
11a, 11b	Solve problems involving fractional parts of a region.	Number and Numeration Goal 2
11c	Rename a fraction as a percent.	Number and Numeration Goal 5
11d, 11e	Predict the outcomes of spinner experiments.	Data and Chance Goal 4
12	Use strategies to find the areas of a rectangle, parallelogram, and triangle.	Measurement and Reference Frames Goal 2

Problem(s)	Description, *continued*	Grade-Level Goal
13	Calculate the volume of a rectangular prism.	Measurement and Reference Frames Goal 2
14	Describe relationships among U.S. customary and metric units of length.	Measurement and Reference Frames Goal 3
15	Use ordered pairs of numbers to locate and plot points on a coordinate grid.	Measurement and Reference Frames Goal 4
16	Estimate the measures of angles.	Measurement and Reference Frames Goal 1
17	Identify geometric solids.	Geometry Goal 2
18	Identify reflections, rotations, and translations.	Geometry Goal 3
19	Complete a pattern and describe a rule.	Patterns, Functions, and Algebra Goal 1
20	Insert parentheses to make true number sentences.	Patterns, Functions, and Algebra Goal 3
21	Solve "percent-of" problems.	Number and Numeration Goal 2
22	Rename fractions as decimals and percents.	Number and Numeration Goal 5
23	Compare fractions and decimals less than 1.	Number and Numeration Goal 6
24	Multiply and divide decimals.	Operations and Computation Goal 4
25	Estimate sums and differences of fractions and mixed numbers.	Operations and Computation Goal 5
26	Measure angles with a protractor.	Measurement and Reference Frames Goal 1
27	Interpret a circle graph.	Data and Chance Goal 2

Grade 4 Mid-Year Assessment Goals

The Mid-Year Assessment (pages 106–111) provides an additional opportunity that you may use as part of your balanced assessment plan. It covers some of the important concepts and skills presented in *Fourth Grade Everyday Mathematics.* It should be used to complement the ongoing and periodic assessments that appear within lessons and at the end of units. The following tables provide the goals for all the problems in Part A and Part B of the Mid-Year Assessment.

Part A Recognizing Student Achievement

Problems 1–26 provide summative information and may be used for grading purposes.

Problem(s)	Description	Grade-Level Goal
1	Write whole numbers and decimals written as words with digits.	Number and Numeration Goal 1
2	List factor pairs.	Number and Numeration Goal 3
3	Name the first 10 multiples of a number.	Number and Numeration Goal 3
4	Give equivalent names for a number.	Number and Numeration Goal 4
5	Use extended addition and subtraction facts to solve a "What's My Rule?" problem.	Operations and Computation Goal 1; Patterns, Functions, and Algebra Goal 1
6	Use extended multiplication and division facts to solve a "What's My Rule?" problem.	Operations and Computation Goal 3; Patterns, Functions, and Algebra Goal 1
7, 8	Solve number stories involving the addition and subtraction of decimals.	Operations and Computation Goal 2
9, 10	Solve problems involving the addition and subtraction of multidigit whole numbers.	Operations and Computation Goal 2
11	Multiply a multidigit whole number by a 1-digit whole number.	Operations and Computation Goal 4; Patterns, Functions, and Algebra Goal 4
12	Divide a multidigit whole number by a 1-digit whole number divisor.	Operations and Computation Goal 4
13	Use data to create a bar graph.	Data and Chance Goal 1
14	Find the median, mode, minimum, maximum, and range of a data set.	Data and Chance Goal 2
15–19	Measure and draw line segments to the nearest inch, $\frac{1}{2}$ inch, $\frac{1}{4}$ inch, centimeter, and $\frac{1}{2}$ centimeter.	Measurement and Reference Frames Goal 1

Problem(s)	Description, *continued*	Grade-Level Goal
20	Draw a ray parallel to a given line. Draw a line segment that intersects a given ray and line.	Geometry Goal 1
21	Draw a quadrangle.	Geometry Goal 2
22	Draw a regular polygon.	Geometry Goal 2
23	Draw a trapezoid.	Geometry Goal 2
24	Draw a shape that is not a polygon.	Geometry Goal 2
25	Solve open sentences involving multiplication and division facts.	Operations and Computation Goal 3; Patterns, Functions, and Algebra Goal 2
26	Determine whether number sentences are true or false.	Patterns, Functions, and Algebra Goal 2

Part B Informing Instruction

Problems 27–33 provide formative information that can be useful in planning future instruction.

Problem(s)	Description	Grade-Level Goal
27	Compare whole numbers and whole numbers represented in exponential notation.	Number and Numeration Goal 6
28	Rename decimals as fractions.	Number and Numeration Goal 5
29, 30	Multiply a multidigit whole number by a 2-digit whole number.	Operations and Computation Goal 4; Patterns, Functions, and Algebra Goal 4
31	Divide a multidigit whole number by a 2-digit divisor.	Operations and Computation Goal 4
32	Create a data set with a given mean.	Data and Chance Goal 2
33	Describe relationships among U.S. customary and metric units of length.	Measurement and Reference Frames Goal 3

Grade 4 End-of-Year Assessment Goals

The End-of-Year Assessment (pages 112–119) provides an additional opportunity that you may use as part of your balanced assessment plan. It covers many of the important concepts and skills presented in *Fourth Grade Everyday Mathematics*. It should be used to complement the ongoing and periodic assessments that appear within lessons and at the end of units. The following tables provide the goals for all the problems in Part A and Part B of the End-of-Year Assessment.

Part A Recognizing Student Achievement

Problems 1–20 provide summative information and may be used for grading purposes.

Problem(s)	Description	Grade-Level Goal
1	Solve problems involving fractional parts of a collection.	Number and Numeration Goal 2
2	Find multiples.	Number and Numeration Goal 3
3	Find factors.	Number and Numeration Goal 3
4	Rename fractions as decimals and percents.	Number and Numeration Goal 5
5	Compare fractions.	Number and Numeration Goal 6
6	Order fractions.	Number and Numeration Goal 6
7a, 7b	Multiply a multidigit whole number by a 2-digit whole number.	Operations and Computation Goal 4
7c, 7d	Divide a multidigit whole number by 1-digit whole number.	Operations and Computation Goal 4
8a, 8b	Add fractions.	Operations and Computation Goal 5
8c, 8d	Subtract fractions.	Operations and Computation Goal 5
9	Use given data to create a line graph.	Data and Chance Goal 1
10	Describe events using basic probability terms.	Data and Chance Goal 3
11a, 11b	Solve problems involving fractional parts of a region.	Number and Numeration Goal 2
11c	Rename a fraction as a percent.	Number and Numeration Goal 5
11d, 11e	Predict the outcomes of spinner experiments.	Data and Chance Goal 4
12	Use strategies to find the areas of a rectangle, parallelogram, and triangle.	Measurement and Reference Frames Goal 2

Problem(s)	Description, *continued*	Grade-Level Goal
13	Calculate the volume of a rectangular prism.	Measurement and Reference Frames Goal 2
14	Describe relationships among U.S. customary and metric units of length.	Measurement and Reference Frames Goal 3
15	Use ordered pairs of numbers to locate and plot points on a coordinate grid.	Measurement and Reference Frames Goal 4
16	Estimate the measures of angles.	Measurement and Reference Frames Goal 1
17	Identify geometric solids.	Geometry Goal 2
18	Identify reflections, rotations, and translations.	Geometry Goal 3
19	Complete a pattern and describe a rule.	Patterns, Functions, and Algebra Goal 1
20	Insert parentheses to make true number sentences.	Patterns, Functions, and Algebra Goal 3

Part B Informing Instruction

Problems 21–27 provide formative information.

Problem(s)	Description	Grade-Level Goal
21	Solve "percent-of" problems.	Number and Numeration Goal 2
22	Rename fractions as decimals and percents.	Number and Numeration Goal 5
23	Compare fractions and decimals less than 1.	Number and Numeration Goal 6
24	Multiply and divide decimals.	Operations and Computation Goal 4
25	Estimate sums and differences of fractions and mixed numbers.	Operations and Computation Goal 5
26	Measure angles with a protractor.	Measurement and Reference Frames Goal 1
27	Interpret a circle graph.	Data and Chance Goal 2

Grade 5 Beginning-of-Year Assessment Goals

The Beginning-of-Year Assessment (pages 120–127) provides an additional opportunity that you may use as part of your balanced plan. It covers many of the important concepts and skills presented in *Fifth Grade Everyday Mathematics*. Since the Beginning-of-Year Assessment parallels the End-of-Year Assessment, it can be used to establish a baseline for measuring students' growth over the year. The Beginning-of-Year Assessment can provide valuable formative assessment information to help teachers tailor instruction to fit their students' needs. The following tables provide goals for all the problems in the Beginning-of-Year Assessment.

Problem(s)	Description	Grade-Level Goal
1	Describe and compare plane figures.	Geometry Goal 2
2	Identify a data set for given landmarks.	Data and Chance Goal 2
3, 19	Represent whole numbers and decimals using expanded notation. Identify the places of a decimal and the value of the digits in those places.	Number and Numeration Goal 1
4, 24–29	Solve problems involving multiplication, division of whole numbers, and decimals.	Operations and Computation Goal 3
5, 30–32	Subtract fractions and add and subtract mixed numbers.	Operations and Computation Goal 4
6	Add fractions and compare the sum to 1.	Operations and Computation Goal 6
7	Convert between base-ten, exponential, and repeated-factor notations.	Number and Numeration Goal 4
8, 9, 10	Calculate the area and perimeter of polygons.	Measurement and Reference Frames Goal 2
11	Insert parentheses to make number sentences true.	Patterns, Functions, and Algebra Goal 3
12	Describe the multiplicative and additive inverses.	Patterns, Functions, and Algebra Goal 4
13, 35–40	Identify equivalent names for fractions, decimals, and percents. Find fractions and mixed numbers in simplest form.	Number and Numeration Goal 5
14, 15, 16, 42–44	Compare fractions, mixed numbers, decimals, and rational numbers.	Number and Numeration Goal 6
17	Use ordered number pairs to plot points in all four quadrants of a coordinate grid.	Measurement and Reference Frames Goal 4
18a, 18b	Describe transformations.	Geometry Goal 3
20, 21	Express the probability of an event as a fraction, decimal, or percent.	Data and Chance Goal 4
22, 33	Use a tool to estimate the measure of angles. Identify lengths to the nearest $\frac{1}{16}$ inch.	Measurement and Reference Frames Goal 1
23	Identify a reflex angle.	Geometry Goal 1

Problem(s)	Description, *continued*	Grade-Level Goal
34	Find the prime factorization.	Number and Numeration Goal 3
41	Use the ratio of parts of a set to find the whole set.	Operations and Computation Goal 7
45–47	Compare expressions involving the addition and subtraction of whole numbers.	Number and Numeration Goal 6; Operations and Computation Goal 1
48, 49	Determine whether number sentences are true or false. Write and solve an open number sentence to model a number story.	Patterns, Functions, and Algebra Goal 2
50	Complete and then graph a function table.	Patterns, Functions, and Algebra Goal 1
51–52	Calculate the volume of a prism and a cylinder.	Operations and Computation Goal 3; Measurement and Reference Frames Goal 2
53–56	Use multiplication and division rules to find equivalent fractions.	Number and Numeration Goal 5
57–60	Use standard notation, scientific notation, and number-and-word notation to represent whole numbers and decimals.	Number and Numeration Goal 1
61	Solve a problem involving percents and discounts.	Number and Numeration Goal 2
66	Calculate and compare the volumes of a prism, a pyramid, and a cone. Calculate circumference and area of a circle.	Measurement and Reference Frames Goal 2
62–65	Find the greatest common factor and the least common multiple for pairs of numbers.	Number and Numeration Goal 3
67–68	Multiply and divide fractions and mixed numbers.	Operations and Computation Goal 5

Grade 5 Mid-Year Assessment Goals

The Mid-Year Assessment (pages 128–133) provides an additional opportunity that you may use as part of your balanced assessment plan. It covers some of the important concepts and skills presented in *Fifth Grade Everyday Mathematics*. It should be used to complement the ongoing and periodic assessments that appear within lessons and at the end of units. The following tables provide goals for all the problems in Part A and Part B of the Mid-Year Assessment

Part A Recognizing Student Achievement

Problems 1–34 provide summative information and may be used for grading purposes.

Problem(s)	Description	Grade-Level Goal
1	Multiply a 2-digit whole number by a 1-digit whole number.	Operations and Computation Goal 3
2	Multiply a 2-digit whole number by a 2-digit whole number.	Operations and Computation Goal 3
3	Multiply a multidigit whole number by a 2-digit whole number.	Operations and Computation Goal 3
4, 5, 6, 7, 8, 9	Solve problems involving the addition and subtraction of multidigit whole numbers and fractions.	Operations and Computation Goal 1
10, 11, 12	Solve open number sentences.	Patterns, Functions, and Algebra Goal 2
13	Identify factors.	Number and Numeration Goal 3
14, 15, 16, 17, 18, 19	Identify and use the minimum, maximum, median, and range to answer questions and draw conclusions.	Data and Chance Goal 2
20	Compare and order fractions and decimals.	Number and Numeration Goal 6
21	Solve number stories involving the addition and subtraction of decimals.	Operations and Computation Goal 1
22	Identify a number that is divisible by 3 but not by 2.	Number and Numeration Goal 3
23	Identify prime and composite numbers.	Number and Numeration Goal 3
24	Identify numerical expressions that represent equivalent names for a fraction.	Number and Numeration Goal 5
25	Identify the places of whole numbers and decimals and the value of the digits in those places.	Number and Numeration Goal 1
26, 27, 28, 29	Add fractions with unlike denominators.	Operations and Computation Goal 4

Problem(s)	Description, *continued*	Grade-Level Goal
30	Identify errors in a multidigit multiplication problem.	Operations and Computation Goal 3
31	Make a magnitude estimate for the product of a multidigit multiplication problem.	Operations and Computation Goal 6
32, 33, 34	Use a graph to answer questions.	Operations and Computation Goal 7; Data and Chance Goal 2

Part B Informing Instruction

Problems 35–45 provide formative information that can be useful in planning future instruction.

Problem(s)	Description	Grade-Level Goal
35	Find the prime factorization.	Number and Numeration Goal 3
36	Estimate length to the nearest millimeter to draw a rectangle given base and height.	Measurement and Reference Frames Goal 1
37	Find the perimeter of a rectangle.	Measurement and Reference Frames Goal 2
38	Use a tool to estimate the measure of angles.	Measurement and Reference Frames Goal 1
39	Identify an obtuse angle.	Geometry Goal 1
40	Use ordered number pairs to plot points in the first quadrant of a coordinate grid.	Measurement and Reference Frames Goal 4
41, 42	Describe a plane figure.	Geometry Goal 2
43	Represent numbers using expanded notation.	Number and Numeration Goal 1
44	Identify and compare a rounded decimal.	Number and Numeration Goals 1 and 6
45	Write fractions and mixed numbers in simplest form.	Number and Numeration Goal 5

Grade 5 End-of-Year Assessment Goals

The End-of-Year Assessment (pages 134–131) provides an additional opportunity that you may use as part of your balanced assessment plan. It covers many of the important concepts and skills presented in *Fifth Grade Everyday Mathematics*. It should be used to complement the ongoing and periodic assessments that appear within lessons and at the end of units. The following tables provide goals for all the problems in Part A and Part B of the End-of-Year Assessment.

Part A Recognizing Student Achievement

Problems 1–52 provide summative information and may be used for grading purposes.

Problem(s)	Description	Grade-Level Goal
1	Describe and compare plane figures.	Geometry Goal 2
2	Identify a data set for given landmarks.	Data and Chance Goal 2
3, 19	Represent whole numbers and decimals using expanded notation. Identify the places of a decimal and the value of the digits in those places.	Number and Numeration Goal 1
4, 24–29	Solve problems involving multiplication, division of whole numbers, and decimals.	Operations and Computation Goal 3
5, 30–32	Subtract fractions and add and subtract mixed numbers.	Operations and Computation Goal 4
6	Add fractions and compare the sum to 1.	Operations and Computation Goal 6
7	Convert between base-ten, exponential, and repeated-factor notations.	Number and Numeration Goal 4
8, 9, 10	Calculate the area and perimeter of polygons.	Measurement and Reference Frames Goal 2
11	Insert parentheses to make number sentences true.	Patterns, Functions, and Algebra Goal 3
12	Describe the multiplicative and additive inverses.	Patterns, Functions, and Algebra Goal 4
13, 35–40	Identify equivalent names for fractions, decimals, and percents. Find fractions and mixed numbers in simplest form.	Number and Numeration Goal 5
14, 15, 16, 42–44	Compare fractions, mixed numbers, decimals, and rational numbers.	Number and Numeration Goal 6
17	Use ordered number pairs to plot points in all four quadrants of a coordinate grid.	Measurement and Reference Frames Goal 4
18a, 18b	Describe transformations.	Geometry Goal 3
20, 21	Express the probability of an event as a fraction, decimal, or percent.	Data and Chance Goal 4
22, 33	Use a tool to estimate the measure of angles. Identify lengths to the nearest $\frac{1}{16}$ inch.	Measurement and Reference Frames Goal 1
23	Identify a reflex angle.	Geometry Goal 1

Problem(s)	Description, *continued*	Grade-Level Goal
34	Find the prime factorization.	Number and Numeration Goal 3
41	Use the ratio of parts of a set to find the whole set.	Operations and Computation Goal 7
45–47	Compare expressions involving the addition and subtraction of whole numbers.	Number and Numeration Goal 6; Operations and Computation Goal 1
48, 49	Determine whether number sentences are true or false. Write and solve an open number sentence to model a number story.	Patterns, Functions, and Algebra Goal 2
50	Complete and then graph a function table.	Patterns, Functions, and Algebra Goal 1
51–52	Calculate the volume of a prism and a cylinder.	Operations and Computation Goal 3; Measurement and Reference Frames Goal 2

Part B Informing Instruction

Problems 53–68 provide formative information.

Problem(s)	Description	Grade-Level Goal
53–56	Use multiplication and division rules to find equivalent fractions.	Number and Numeration Goal 5
57–60	Use standard notation, scientific notation, and number-and-word notation to represent whole numbers and decimals.	Number and Numeration Goal 1
61	Solve a problem involving percents and discounts.	Number and Numeration Goal 2
66	Calculate and compare the volumes of a prism, a pyramid, and a cone. Calculate circumference and area of a circle.	Measurement and Reference Frames Goal 2
62–65	Find the greatest common factor and the least common multiple for pairs of numbers.	Number and Numeration Goal 3
67–68	Multiply and divide fractions and mixed numbers.	Operations and Computation Goal 5

Grade 6 Beginning-of-Year Assessment Goals

The Beginning-of-Year Assessment (pages 142–150) provides an additional opportunity that you may use as part of your balanced assessment plan. It covers some of the important concepts and skills presented in *Sixth Grade Everyday Mathematics*. Since the Beginning-of-Year Assessment parallels the End-of-Year Assessment, it can be used to establish a baseline for measuring students' growth over the year. The Beginning-of-Year Assessment can provide valuable formative assessment information to help you tailor instruction to fit students' needs. The following tables provide goals for all the problems in the Beginning-of-Year Assessment.

Problem(s)	Description	Grade-Level Goal
1a–1d	Use expanded, number-and-word, exponential, and scientific notation to represent whole numbers and decimals.	Number and Numeration Goal 1
1	Apply place-value concepts to compare numbers.	Number and Numeration Goals 1 and 6
1e, 1f, 20, 21	Convert between fractions, decimals, and percents.	Number and Numeration Goal 5
2a–c	Divide fractions and mixed numbers.	Operations and Computation Goal 4
3a, 3b, 27–30	Apply the order of operations to evaluate an expression.	Patterns, Functions, and Algebra Goal 3
4a, 4b	Estimate quotients of decimal numbers.	Operations and Computation Goal 5
5	Complete a table for a given rule. Plot and connect points to make a line graph.	Patterns, Functions, and Algebra Goal 1; Measurement and Reference Frames Goal 3
6a, 6b	Add signed numbers.	Operations and Computation Goal 1
6c, 6d, 15b	Multiply and divide whole, decimal, and signed numbers.	Operations and Computation Goal 2
7a–d	Determine whether equalities and inequalities are true or false.	Patterns, Functions, and Algebra Goal 2
8–11, 27–30	Solve linear equations having one unknown on one side and each side of the equal sign. Combine like terms.	Patterns, Functions, and Algebra Goal 2
12a, 12b	Graph the solution set for an inequality.	Patterns, Functions, and Algebra Goal 2
13a	Make a list or tree diagram to identify all possible outcomes.	Data and Chance Goal 3
13b	Calculate a probability. Express the probability as a percent.	Data and Chance Goal 3
14	Apply theoretical probability to make predictions.	Data and Chance Goal 3
15, 18b, 19d	Use ratios to solve scaling/size-change problems.	Operations and Computation Goal 6
15a, 15c	Apply equivalent names for fractions to convert between units of customary measure.	Number and Numeration Goal 5

Problem(s)	Description, *continued*	Grade-Level Goal
16a	Solve problems involving rates. Divide decimal numbers.	Operations and Computation Goals 2 and 6
16b	Model rate number stories using division or proportions.	Operations and Computation Goal 6
17	Solve problems involving part-to-whole ratios.	Operations and Computation Goal 6
18a	Measure length to the nearest millimeter.	Measurement and Reference Frames Goal 1
18a, 19a–d	Apply properties of similar figures.	Geometry Goal 2
19a	Name ordered pairs of numbers on a coordinate grid.	Measurement and Reference Frames Goal 3
19b, 19d, 27, 28	Calculate the area and perimeter of a figure.	Measurement and Reference Frames Goal 2
19c, 27–30	Use appropriate formulas to solve problems.	Measurement and Reference Frames Goal 2
19d	Explain strategies to solve size-change problems.	Operations and Computation Goal 6
21	Simplify fractions.	Number and Numeration Goals 3 and 5
22–26	Calculate the percent of a number. Identify the whole when a percent is given.	Number and Numeration Goal 2
30	Multiply whole numbers and fractions.	Operations and Computation Goal 4
29, 30	Calculate the volume of a solid.	Measurement and Reference Frames Goal 2
27–30	Write an equation to represent a geometric situation.	Patterns, Functions, and Algebra Goal 1
31a–e	Apply definitions and properties of angles, triangles, and quadrangles to determine angle measures. Apply vertical and supplementary angle relationships to determine the measures of angles without using a protractor.	Geometry Goal 1
32	Plot and label points in all four quadrants of a coordinate grid.	Measurement and Reference Frames Goal 3
32	Apply the knowledge that a preimage and its image are congruent.	Geometry Goal 2
32	Translate and reflect a figure on a coordinate grid.	Geometry Goal 3
33	Identify and describe instances of reflections, translations, and rotations.	Geometry Goal 3
34a	Write an equation to calculate a perimeter.	Patterns, Functions, and Algebra Goal 1; Measurement and Reference Frames Goal 2
34c	Evaluate an expression.	Patterns, Functions, and Algebra Goal 3
34, 35	Solve linear equations having one unknown on each side of the equal sign.	Patterns, Functions, and Algebra Goal 2
35	Apply distributive strategies to solve problems.	Patterns, Functions, and Algebra Goal 4

Grade 6 Mid-Year Assessment Goals

The Mid-Year Assessment (pages 151–158) provides an additional opportunity that you may use as part of your balanced assessment plan. It covers some of the important concepts and skills presented in *Sixth Grade Everyday Mathematics*. It should be used to complement the ongoing and periodic assessments that appear within lessons and at the end of units. The following tables provide goals for all the problems in Part A and Part B of the Mid-Year Assessment.

Part A Recognizing Student Achievement

Problems 1–24 provide summative information and may be used for grading purposes.

Problem(s)	Description	Grade-Level Goal
1a	Construct a stem-and-leaf plot	Data and Chance Goal 1
1b, 2	Identify and analyze data landmarks. Compare the median and mean values of a data set.	Data and Chance Goal 2
3a, 3b	Interpret data represented by a stacked bar graph.	Data and Chance Goal 1
3c	Estimate a fractional part of a region.	Number and Numeration Goal 2
4–6	Use expanded, number-and-word, exponential, and scientific notation to represent whole numbers and decimals.	Number and Numeration Goal 1
7, 8	Add and subtract decimals.	Operations and Computation Goal 1
9, 10	Divide a whole number by 2- and 3-digit divisors.	Operations and Computation Goal 2
11	Complete a table for a given rule.	Patterns, Functions, and Algebra Goal 1
12	Plot and connect points to make a line graph.	Measurement and Reference Frames Goal 3
13, 14	Analyze a real-world situation by making and using a table of data and a related graph.	Patterns, Functions, and Algebra Goal 1
15	Order fractions and decimals.	Number and Numeration Goal 6
16a–16c	Add and subtract fractions and mixed numbers.	Operations and Computation Goal 3
16d	Multiply mixed numbers.	Operations and Computation Goal 4
16, 17	Find equivalent fractions and fractions in simplest form; convert between fractions, decimals, and percents.	Number and Numeration Goal 5
18–20	Solve problems involving fractions, decimals, and percents; calculate fractional parts and percents of numbers.	Number and Numeration Goal 2
19	Use a protractor to draw angles with given measures to make a circle graph.	Data and Chance Goal 1

Problem(s)	Description, *continued*	Grade-Level Goal
21	Write an algebraic expression to describe a situation.	Patterns, Functions, and Algebra Goal 1
22	Evaluate an expression.	Patterns, Functions, and Algebra Goal 3
23, 24	Apply definitions and properties of angles, triangles, and quadrangles to determine angle measures. Apply vertical and supplementary angle relationships to determine the measures of angles.	Geometry Goal 1

Part B Informing Instruction

Problems 25–35 provide formative information that can be used in planning future instruction.

Problem(s)	Description	Grade-Level Goal
25, 26	Plot and label points in all four quadrants of a coordinate grid.	Measurement and Reference Frames Goal 3
26, 27	Apply the knowledge that a preimage and its image are congruent.	Geometry Goal 2
26, 27	Translate and reflect a figure on a coordinate grid.	Geometry Goal 3
28	Identify locations on a spreadsheet. Use spreadsheet cell names to write a formula for calculating a mean.	Patterns, Functions, and Algebra Goal 1
29	Find equivalent fractions.	Number and Numeration Goal 5
30	Draw line segments to the nearest $\frac{1}{16}$ inch.	Measurement and Reference Frames Goal 1
31, 32	Calculate the perimeter and area of a rectangle given the base and height.	Measurement and Reference Frames Goal 2
33	Solve problems involving fractions, decimals, and percents; calculate fractional parts and percents of numbers	Number and Numeration Goal 2
34	Estimate quotients of whole and decimal numbers.	Operations and Computation Goal 5
35	Divide a decimal-number dividend by a whole-number divisor.	Operations and Computation Goal 2

Grade 6 End-of-Year Assessment Goals

The End-of-Year Assessment (pages 159–167) provides an additional opportunity that you may use as part of your balanced assessment plan. It covers some of the important concepts and skills presented in *Sixth Grade Everyday Mathematics*. It should be used to complement the ongoing and periodic assessments that appear within lessons and at the end of units.

Part A Recognizing Student Achievement

Problems 1–32 provide summative information and may be used for grading purposes.

Problem(s)	Description	Grade-Level Goal
1a–1d	Use expanded, number-and-word, exponential, and scientific notation to represent whole numbers and decimals.	Number and Numeration Goal 1
1	Apply place-value concepts to compare numbers.	Number and Numeration Goals 1 and 6
1e, 1f, 20, 21	Convert between fractions, decimals, and percents.	Number and Numeration Goal 5
2a–c	Divide fractions and mixed numbers.	Operations and Computation Goal 4
3a, 3b, 27–30	Apply the order of operations to evaluate an expression.	Patterns, Functions, and Algebra Goal 3
4a, 4b	Estimate quotients of decimal numbers.	Operations and Computation Goal 5
5	Complete a table for a given rule. Plot and connect points to make a line graph.	Patterns, Functions, and Algebra Goal 1; Measurement and Reference Frames Goal 3
6a, 6b	Add signed numbers.	Operations and Computation Goal 1
6c, 6d, 15b	Multiply and divide whole, decimal, and signed numbers.	Operations and Computation Goal 2
7a–d	Determine whether equalities and inequalities are true or false.	Patterns, Functions, and Algebra Goal 2
8–11, 27–30	Solve linear equations having one unknown on one side and each side of the equal sign. Combine like terms.	Patterns, Functions, and Algebra Goal 2
12a, 12b	Graph the solution set for an inequality.	Patterns, Functions, and Algebra Goal 2
13a	Make a list or tree diagram to identify all possible outcomes.	Data and Chance Goal 3
13b	Calculate a probability. Express the probability as a percent.	Data and Chance Goal 3
14	Apply theoretical probability to make predictions.	Data and Chance Goal 3
15, 18b, 19d	Use ratios to solve scaling/size-change problems.	Operations and Computation Goal 6
15a, 15c	Apply equivalent names for fractions to convert between units of customary measure.	Number and Numeration Goal 5

Problem(s)	Description, *continued*	Grade-Level Goal
16a	Solve problems involving rates. Divide decimal numbers.	Operations and Computation Goals 2 and 6
16b	Model rate number stories using division or proportions.	Operations and Computation Goal 6
17	Solve problems involving part-to-whole ratios.	Operations and Computation Goal 6
18a	Measure length to the nearest millimeter.	Measurement and Reference Frames Goal 1
18a, 19a–d	Apply properties of similar figures.	Geometry Goal 2
19a	Name ordered pairs of numbers on a coordinate grid.	Measurement and Reference Frames Goal 3
19b, 19d, 27, 28	Calculate the area and perimeter of a figure.	Measurement and Reference Frames Goal 2
19c, 27–30	Use appropriate formulas to solve problems.	Measurement and Reference Frames Goal 2
19d	Explain strategies to solve size-change problems.	Operations and Computation Goal 6
21	Simplify fractions.	Number and Numeration Goals 3 and 5
22–26	Calculate the percent of a number. Identify the whole when a percent is given.	Number and Numeration Goal 2
30	Multiply whole numbers and fractions.	Operations and Computation Goal 4
29, 30	Calculate the volume of a solid.	Measurement and Reference Frames Goal 2
27–30	Write an equation to represent a geometric situation.	Patterns, Functions, and Algebra Goal 1
31a–e	Apply definitions and properties of angles, triangles, and quadrangles to determine angle measures. Apply vertical and supplementary angle relationships to determine the measures of angles without using a protractor.	Geometry Goal 1
32	Plot and label points in all four quadrants of a coordinate grid.	Measurement and Reference Frames Goal 3
32	Apply the knowledge that a preimage and its image are congruent.	Geometry Goal 2
32	Translate and reflect a figure on a coordinate grid.	Geometry Goal 3

Part B Informing Instruction

Problems 33–35 provide formative information.

Problem(s)	Description	Grade-Level Goal
33	Identify and describe instances of reflections, translations, and rotations.	Geometry Goal 3
34a	Write an equation to calculate a perimeter.	Patterns, Functions, and Algebra Goal 1; Measurement and Reference Frames Goal 2
34c	Evaluate an expression.	Patterns, Functions, and Algebra Goal 3
34, 35	Solve linear equations having one unknown on each side of the equal sign.	Patterns, Functions, and Algebra Goal 2
35	Apply distributive strategies to solve problems.	Patterns, Functions, and Algebra Goal 4

Kindergarten Periodic Assessment Tasks

Suggestions for Baseline Periodic Assessment Tasks

(Activities may be done over several days.)

1. Count on by 1s. [Number and Numeration Goal 1] Ask children to count aloud to 10. Then ask them if they can go any higher. Encourage them to count as high as they can. If a child can count very high, stop and start him or her at various numbers to more efficiently get a sense of how high he or she can count. Look for the point at which the child's counting becomes erratic.

2. Count back by 1s. [Number and Numeration Goal 1] Ask children to count backward from 5 down to 0. If a child can go backward from 5, have him or her start from 10. Note what number the child can count backward from.

3. Count objects. [Number and Numeration Goal 2] Have children count objects such as boys, girls, chairs, balls, crackers, and so on. Embed this task into ongoing classroom experiences by taking advantage of natural counting opportunities, such as setting the table or cleaning up. Look for whether the child can count up to 5, 10, 20, or more objects.

4. Read numbers. [Number and Numeration Goal 3] Give children a plastic bag containing number cards 0–5. Tell them to reach in, find, and then hold up the number you name. (You might say "1, 2, 3, show me!" to set a playful tone and ensure that everyone pulls out their cards at the same time.) Add number cards 6–10 (or beyond) to each bag for children who are ready. Group children of similar abilities together or work with individuals. Look for whether the child can read numerals 0–5, 6–10, or teens or higher.

5. Compare and order numbers. [Number and Numeration Goal 6] Show children two number cards with numbers from 0–5, and ask them to show you the higher number. Add cards through 10 if children seem ready. Look for whether the child can correctly identify the higher number and if he or she uses a reference tool to help compare the numbers.

6. Compare sizes of objects. [Measurement and Reference Frames Goal 1] Ask children to find the "smallest chair in the room" or "a chair bigger (larger) than this one." Note that early in Kindergarten, many children may be more familiar with comparisons using the terms *big, (big, bigger, biggest)* and *little* than with comparisons using *small* and *large*. Consciously use all these terms. Or use a group of toys of varying sizes and ask children to point to the one that is *"largest…," "smaller (littler) than this ball,"* and so on. Look for whether the child correctly identifies objects using size comparison language.

7. Recognize two-dimensional geometric shapes. [Geometry Goal 1] Provide plastic bags containing shape cutouts or attribute block shapes, with two each of circles, triangles, and squares. Have children retrieve the shape you dictate using the "1, 2, 3, show me!" procedure. Alternatively, station yourself at a Center or at the side of the room during a playtime or Center time and call children individually to pick out shapes you name. Note whether the child correctly shows the circle, triangle, and square.

8. Identify shapes having line symmetry. [Geometry Goal 2] Show children a drawing of something symmetrical (such as a symmetrical flower or butterfly) with a vertical line of symmetry drawn on it. Ask if the two sides match. Repeat with a drawing of something that is not symmetrical (also with a line drawn through the middle). Allow children to manipulate the drawing (by touching, folding, and so on) if desired. If children correctly identify left and right matching sides, you might show a symmetrical drawing with a horizontal line of symmetry and top and bottom halves matching, such as a ball with symmetrical markings. Look for whether the child can determine if two sides of an object or drawing match one another.

9. Extend a pattern. [Patterns, Functions, and Algebra Goal 1] Begin a simple movement pattern (clap, snap; clap, snap; clap, snap; and so on) or a color pattern with connecting cubes. Invite children to extend your pattern, and observe what they do. For children who are proficient, you might repeat with a more complicated pattern (for example, clap, clap, snap; clap, clap, snap;...) and see if they can extend it. Note whether the child can correctly extend the pattern you began.

10. Use a rule to sort objects. [Patterns, Functions, and Algebra Goal 1] Give children a bag of objects varying in color, size, and/or shape. Tell them to sort (group) the objects, but do not specify a particular sorting rule. When the task is complete, ask children to explain how they sorted the objects (by size, color, or shape, for example). Specify a sorting criterion (color, size, and so on) and evaluate children's ability to sort according to the rule you provide. Look for whether the child is aware of the different attributes of objects and the concept of sorting.

Notes

_____

_____

_____

_____

_____

_____

_____

_____

Suggestions for Mid-Year Periodic Assessment Tasks

NOTE In addition to determining whether children are making adequate progress toward each Kindergarten goal (as described in the last sentence of each task description below), note the specific level of proficiency they demonstrate with each task.

1. Count on by 1s. [Number and Numeration Goal 1] Start with any number other than 0 or 1, and ask children to count to some specified number. Start counting again from a different number. Continue with higher numbers until the child begins to have difficulty. Allow children who are having difficulty to look at a number line or number grid for reference. Look for the child to count to at least 30 from different starting numbers.

2. Count back by 1s. [Number and Numeration Goal 1] Ask children to count back from 10 to 0. If they do this easily, give a starting number in the low teens and have them count back for a string of several numbers. Gradually increase the starting number. Encourage children to look at a number line or number grid for reference if needed. Look for the child to count back from at least 10 to 0.

3. Count on by 5s and 10s. [Number and Numeration Goal 1] Ask children to start from 0 and skip count by 10s as high as they can. Repeat, this time asking them to skip count by 5s. Children may use a number line or number grid as a reference tool. Look for the child to count on to at least 50 by 10s and by 5s.

4. Count objects. [Number and Numeration Goal 2] Present children with a collection of 10–20 objects, and ask them to count how many you have. For those who are ready, add objects to go above 20 and ask them to count again. Look for the child to count at least 20 objects.

5. Estimate the number of objects in a collection. [Number and Numeration Goal 2] Show children a jar with 10–20 objects and a reference jar with a known quantity (perhaps 10) of the same objects. Ask children to estimate how many are in the estimation jar and explain why they made their estimate. If children make wild guesses, try putting fewer objects in the jar to see whether they are able to estimate (without counting). Look for the child to make an educated, rather than a wild guess to estimate items in a collection, and to explain his or her reasoning.

6. Model numbers with manipulatives. [Number and Numeration Goal 3] Provide straws or craft sticks and rubber bands and ask children to use the materials to represent a number that you name. Begin with a number less than-10. Then try a teen number. Repeat for higher numbers with children who seem ready (those who are bundling sticks and thinking about tens and ones). Look for the child to show a number with single sticks or with bundles of 10 and single sticks.

7. Read and write (or dictate) 2-digit numbers. [Number and Numeration Goal 3] Beginning with numbers in the teens, ask children to tell you how to write 2-digit numbers that you name. Repeat for a number in the 20s and one in the 30s. Then write or point to some 2-digit numbers and ask children to name the numbers. Again, begin with teens and gradually increase. If children seem ready, ask them to name or write 2-digit numbers in the 40s and higher. Look for the child to read and write (or dictate) 2-digit numbers to at least 30.

8. Compare and order numbers. [Number and Numeration Goal 6] Play a few rounds of *Top-It* with children. Begin with 0–10 cards. If children seem ready, add cards through 20. Provide a reference tool to help with comparing numbers for children who need it. Look for the child to identify the higher card for numbers 0–10 or higher in each round of *Top-It*.

9. Solve number stories. [Operations and Computation Goal 1], and **Identify join and take-away situations.** [Operations and Computation Goal 2] Pick a number story page from the middle section (Part 2) of *Minute Math*. Ask children to solve it and observe what strategies they use. Provide manipulatives, number lines, or other tools that children can use to solve the stories. Ask whether it is a join or take-away (addition or subtraction) story. If they seem ready, have children tell a join or take-away story. Look for the child to solve simple addition and subtraction number stories. (They may still have difficulty identifying join and take-away stories.)

10. Describe events using basic probability terms. [Data and Chance Goal-3] Put an assortment of attribute blocks on a tray. Before children pick a block from the tray, ask them questions such as: *Is it possible that you will pick a red square? Are you certain to get a blue block? Are you more likely to pick a blue block or a red block? Why?* (See Activity 3-11 for additional sample questions.) Look for the child to answer questions that are phrased in terms of basic probability terms, such as *certain, possible,* and *impossible.* (Children are not necessarily expected to use *more likely* and *less likely* yet, although many children will.)

11. Use nonstandard tools and techniques to estimate and compare weight and length. [Measurement and Reference Frames Goal 1] Show children a collection of three or more objects, at least two the same size. Ask them to arrange them in order of length. Prompt with questions such as: *Which is the longest? Are any of them the same length? How do you know?* Then ask children to arrange them in order of weight. Invite children to use tools to find out more about the length and weight of the objects. Watch which tools they choose (perhaps connecting cubes and a pan balance) and how they use the tools. For children who have difficulty working with 3 objects at a time, begin with direct comparisons of 2 objects and ask questions such as: *Which is longer? Are they the same length? Which is heavier?* Look for the child to correctly compare the length and weight of objects and to choose and use tools to measure the length and weight of objects.

12. Identify plane (2-dimensional) figures. [Geometry Goal 1] Put a collection of pattern blocks and attribute blocks on a tray. Ask children to remove the shapes you name from the tray. Begin by asking for circles, triangles, rectangles, and squares. Ask children who seem ready for additional shapes, such as hexagons. Look for the child to at least identify circles, triangles, rectangles, and squares.

13. Identify shapes having line symmetry. [Geometry Goal 2] Show children a drawing of something symmetrical, such as a butterfly with symmetrical markings. Ask: *Is it symmetrical? Why (or why not)?* Alternatively, provide several pre-cut shapes (some symmetrical; some not) and have children sort them according to whether or not they are symmetrical. Look for the child to recognize that both sides must match if an object is symmetrical.

14. Extend, describe, and create patterns. [Patterns, Functions, and Algebra Goal 1] Ask children to create a pattern with pattern blocks and to describe their patterns. If children create a 2-part pattern, continue by asking them to extend a 3-part pattern that you create. (For example: show triangle, hexagon, diamond; triangle, hexagon, diamond; …). Ask children if they can create and describe a more complicated pattern. Look for the child to create and/or extend 2- and 3-part patterns and describe the patterns.

15. Use a rule to sort objects. [Patterns, Functions, and Algebra Goal 1] Have children sort a collection of attribute blocks according to an attribute that you specify (size, shape, color, or thickness). When they complete this task, ask them to sort again using another attribute of their choice. Look for the child to sort blocks by a given attribute and by an attribute of their choice.

Notes

_____

_____

_____

_____

_____

_____

_____

_____

_____

_____

_____

_____

Suggestions for End-of-Year Periodic Assessment Tasks

NOTE In addition to determining whether children are making adequate progress toward each Kindergarten goal (as described in the last sentence of each task description below), note the specific level of proficiency they demonstrate with each task.

1. Count on by 1s. [Number and Numeration Goal 1] Start with any number other than 0 or 1 and ask children to count to some specified number. Start counting again from a different number. Continue until the child begins to have difficulty. Look for the child to count to at least 100 from various numbers.

2. Count back by 1s. [Number and Numeration Goal 1] Ask children to count back from a number in at least the teens or twenties. Invite them to use a reference tool, such as a number line or number grid, if needed. Look for the child to count back by 1s from a number beyond 10.

3. Count on by 2s, 5s and 10s. [Number and Numeration Goal 1] Ask children to start from 0 and skip count by 2s as high as they can. Repeat, this time asking them to skip count by 10s, then by 5s. Children may use a number line or number grid as a reference tool. Look for the child to count on by 2s, by 5s, and by 10s.

4. Count objects. [Number and Numeration Goal 2] Present children with a collection of 10–20 objects, and ask them to count how many you have. For those who are ready, add more objects. Look for the child to count at least 20 objects in a collection.

5. Estimate the number of objects in a collection. [Number and Numeration Goal 2] Show children a jar with 10–20 objects and a reference jar with a known quantity (perhaps 10) of the same objects. Ask children to estimate how many are in the estimation jar and explain why they made their estimate. For children who are ready, use more than 20 objects in the estimate jar. Look for the child to make an educated guess, rather than a wild guess, to estimate items in a collection, and to explain his or her reasoning.

6. Model numbers with manipulatives. [Number and Numeration Goal 3] Provide single straws or craft sticks, as well as some bundles of 10. Ask children to use the materials to represent numbers that you name. Begin with a teen number and see if they use a bundle of 10 and single sticks. (Some children may count out the number of single sticks without using a bundle of 10. Ask these children if they can make the number using a bundle.) Repeat for higher numbers with children who can easily do teen numbers. Include a big bundle of 100 sticks or straws and ask for a number in the 100s for children who are ready. Look for the child to show a teen or higher number using bundles of 10 sticks and one or more single sticks.

7. Exchange 1s for 10s and 10s for 100. [Number and Numeration Goal 3] Provide rubber bands and a large number of craft sticks (at least 30; not an even 10). Invite children to make bundles of 10 or exchanges with pre-bundled sticks. Have them count the total by 10s and 1s. Next, show 10 bundles of 10 craft sticks and ask children what they could trade it for. Look for the child to exchange 1s for 10s and 10s for 100.

8. Read and write (or dictate) 2-digit numbers. [Number and Numeration Goal 3] Ask children to tell you how to write 2-digit numbers that you name. Then write or point to some 2-digit numbers and ask children to name the numbers. Start with numbers below 30, then increase. For children who are ready, move to writing and reading 3-digit numbers. Look for the child to read and write (or dictate) 2-digit numbers through at least 30.

9. Use manipulatives to model half of a region or collection. [Number and Numeration Goal 4] Give children a cracker or picture of a cracker. Have them divide it in half. Also give an even-numbered collection of items for children to divide in half. Ask children to explain why what they've made are called *halves*. Look for the child to model and describe half of a region or collection and to understand that the two halves should be the same size.

10. Give equivalent names for numbers. [Number and Numeration Goal 5] Ask children to create a name collection for the number 15. (Use a lower number if 15 seems too high for some.) Probe to expand the different types of representations they include, as needed. If children are ready, ask them to create a name collection for a number in the 20s. Look for the child to use maniulatives, drawings, and numerical expressions involving addition and subtraction of 1-digit numbers to give equivalent names for numbers up to at least 20. Note whether they understand that numbers can be represented in different ways.

11. Compare and order numbers. [Number and Numeration Goal 6] Play *Top-It* with children. Use 0–20 cards. After the game, select three cards and ask children to order them from smallest to largest. Look for the child to compare and order numbers up to at least 20.

12. Solve number stories. [Operations and Computation Goal 1], **Identify join and take-away situations.** [Operations and Computation Goal 2], and **Read and write expressions and number sentences using the symbols +, −, and =.** [Patterns, Functions, and Algebra Goal 2] Pick addition and subtraction number story pages from the middle or last section of *Minute Math*. Ask children to solve the stories and observe what strategies they use. (Provide manipulatives, number lines, or other tools.) Ask whether each story is a join or take-away (addition or subtraction) story. Also have the children write a number model to match each number story or enter the problem on a calculator.

Look for the child to use manipulatives, number lines, and mental arithmetic to solve number stories and to identify join and take-away situations. Also look for the child to use +, −, and = symbols to read and write expressions and number sentences to model the stories.

13. Use graphs to answer simple questions. [Data and Chance Goal 2] Show a familiar graph (a class graph or a child's survey graph). Ask some questions about the graph. Begin with basic questions, such as: *What does this graph tell us? Which category has the most (and least)?* If the children are ready, progress to more difficult questions, such as comparing two categories. *(Which is more?)* For children who seem ready, you might ask: *How many more?* Look for the child to use graphs to answer simple questions.

14. Describe events using basic probability terms. [Data and Chance Goal-3] Put an assortment of red and blue attribute blocks on a tray. Before children pick a block from the tray, ask them questions, such as: *Is it possible that you will pick a red block? Are you certain to pick a red block? Are you more likely to pick a blue block or a red block? Why?* (See Activity 3-11 for additional sample questions.) Look for the child to describe events using *certain, possible, impossible,* and other basic probability terms.

15. Use nonstandard tools and techniques to estimate and compare weight and length. [Measurement and Reference Frames Goal 1] Set out a collection of objects and ask children: *Which is longest? How can you check? Which is heaviest? How can you check?* Watch their choices of tools and use of measuring techniques. Look for the child to use nonstandard tools and techniques to estimate and compare length and weight.

16. Identify pennies, nickels, dimes, quarters, and dollar bills. [Measurement and Reference Frames Goal 2] Show a mixed collection of money (pennies, nickels, dimes, quarters, and a dollar bill). Ask children to find each coin or bill you name. Ask whether they know the value of each. For some children, you might invite them to make some trades. *(Which coin could I trade these five pennies for? Do you want to trade anything for this dime?)* Look for the child to correctly identify a penny, nickel, dime, quarter, and dollar bill.

17. Identify standard measuring tools. [Measurement and Reference Frames Goals 1, 3, and 4] Show children a thermometer, analog clock, pan balance, and ruler (or a picture of these tools). Ask: *Which tool would you use to measure temperature? Which would you use to measure time? Length? Weight?* You might also ask children to tell you what other tools they know of to measure time, temperature, length, and weight. Look for the child to identify tools for measuring temperature, time, weight, and length.

18. Describe and use time periods relative to a day and week. [Measurement and Reference Frames Goal 4] With your class calendar and daily schedule available for reference, ask children questions such as the following:

◆ *Name something we will do this morning (or afternoon).*
◆ *What will we do after that?*
◆ *Point to today on the calendar. What day is today?*
◆ *Point to yesterday (or tomorrow). What day was yesterday (will tomorrow be)?*

Tailor the difficulty of your questions to children's level of understanding. Look for the child to use terms such as morning, afternoon, yesterday, today, tomorrow, and sequencing words to describe time periods relative to a day and week.

19. Identify 2-dimensional shapes and 3-dimensional solids. [Geometry Goal 1] Ask: *Can you find a sphere in the classroom? A cube?* Include other 3-D shapes if children are ready. Begin with 2-dimensional shapes for children who struggled with this during previous assessments. Look for the child to identify a circle, triangle, square, rectangle, sphere, and cube.

20. Identify shapes having line symmetry. [Geometry Goal 2] Show children a drawing of something symmetrical, such as a butterfly with symmetrical markings. Ask: *Is it symmetrical? Why (or why not)?* Alternatively, provide several pre-cut shapes (some symmetrical; some not) and have children sort them according to whether or not they are symmetrical. Look for the child to recognize that both sides must match if an object is symmetrical and to identify objects having line symmetry.

21. Extend, describe, and create patterns. [Patterns, Functions, and Algebra Goal 1] Ask children to create a pattern with pattern blocks and to describe it. If children create a 2-part pattern, continue by asking them to extend a 3-part pattern that you create (for example: triangle, hexagon, diamond; triangle, hexagon, diamond; …). Ask them to extend your pattern. Ask children if they can create and describe a more complicated pattern. Look for the child to create and/or extend 2- and 3-part patterns and describe the patterns.

22. Use a rule to sort objects. [Patterns, Functions, and Algebra Goal 1] Have children sort a collection of attribute blocks according to an attribute that you specify (size, shape, color, or thickness). When they complete this task, ask them to sort again using another attribute of their choice. Look for the child to use rules to sort in different ways.

23. Use rules for *"What's My Rule?" Fishing*. [Patterns, Functions, and Algebra Goal 1] Play *"What's My Rule?" Fishing* in large or small groups. Ensure that all children get a chance to guess the rule over a period of time. Look for the child to understand the basic concept behind "What's My Rule?" activities.

Notes

_____

_____

_____

_____

_____

_____

_____

_____

GRADE 1 **Beginning-of-Year Assessment**

1. Shade the fraction for each shape.

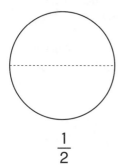   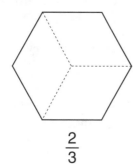   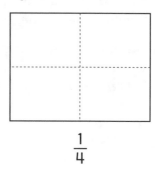

$\frac{1}{2}$ $\frac{2}{3}$ $\frac{1}{4}$

2. Use <, >, and =.

34 ☐ 43   8 + 4 ☐ 5 + 7

22 ☐ 10 + 10   67 ☐ 78

> < is less than
> > is more than
> = is equal to

3. Use the word bank to help you write the name for each shape.

| rectangle | circle | pyramid | cone | square | cube | sphere |

_____   _____   _____

                    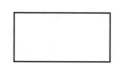

_____   _____   _____

GRADE 1

Beginning-of-Year Assessment *cont.*

4. Add or subtract.

2 + 3 = _____   10   18   3
                        −8   −1   −3
11 − 1 = _____   ____   ____   ____

8 + _____ = 12

_____ = 9 − 4

_____ + 0 = 19

0 + _____ = 19

5. What is your favorite flavor of fruit drink?
Add your vote to the graph.

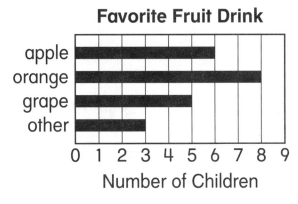

Favorite Fruit Drink

Number of Children

What flavor is least

popular? _____

What flavor is most

popular? _____

How many children like grape drink? _____

6. Circle the symmetrical picture.

Beginning-of-Year Assessment *cont.*

7. What letter are you most likely to spin? _____

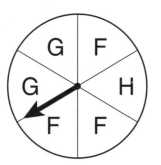

8. What is the temperature? _____ °F

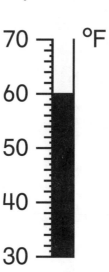

9. Measure the line segment to the nearest centimeter.

_____   about _____ cm

10. Write 3 names for 40.

Label the box.
Put 3 new names in the box.

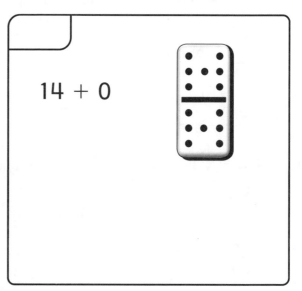

14 + 0

11. Draw the hands.

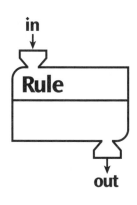

2:45

quarter after 6 o'clock

12. Ⓠ Ⓓ Ⓓ Ⓓ Ⓝ Ⓝ Ⓟ Ⓟ   How much money?   _____ ¢

Show this amount with fewer coins.

13. Find the rule. Fill in the table.

in	out
9	5
25	21
	26
46	
104	

in
↓
Rule
out

GRADE 1

Beginning-of-Year Assessment *cont.*

14. Write the numbers shown by the base-10 blocks.

 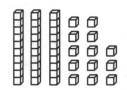 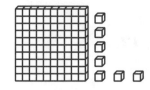

_____   _____   _____

Draw a ◯ around the ones place. Draw a △ around the tens place.

15. Sara has $1 Ⓠ Ⓠ Ⓓ Ⓓ Ⓝ Ⓟ Ⓟ Ⓟ $_ ___

Luis has $1 Ⓓ Ⓓ Ⓓ Ⓝ Ⓝ Ⓟ Ⓟ Ⓟ $_ ___

Who has more money? _____

How much more money? _____

16. Two people share these marbles equally.

How many marbles does each person get?

_____ marbles

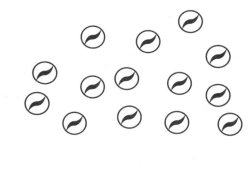

17. Solve. You may use your number grid.

$$\begin{array}{r} 46 \\ -13 \\ \hline \end{array} \qquad \begin{array}{r} 59 \\ +30 \\ \hline \end{array} \qquad \begin{array}{r} 28 \\ -13 \\ \hline \end{array}$$

Beginning-of-Year Assessment *cont.*

18. Add.

3 + 4 = _____   10 + 6 = _____

30 + 40 = _____   20 + 6 = _____

300 + 400 = _____   30 + 6 = _____

19. Solve.
Jack found 19 rocks at the lake.
Rosa found 30 rocks at the lake.
How many rocks did Jack and Rosa find in all?

_____ rocks

Write a number model.

20. What time is it?

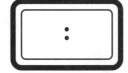

LESSON 5·14 | Mid-Year Assessment

Part A

1.

How many ☐s? _____

Even or odd? _____

How many ☐s? _____

Even or odd? _____

2. Complete this part of the number grid.

		13		15					20
	22					27	28		
31			34		36			39	

3. Count by 2s.

2, _____, _____, _____, _____, _____

Count by 10s.

20, _____, _____, _____, _____, _____

4. Draw what comes next.

LESSON 5·14 **Mid-Year Assessment** *continued*

5. Draw the hands.

5 o'clock

half-past
3 o'clock

half-past
11 o'clock

6. Measure the line segment to the nearest inch.

————————————— about _____ inches

7. Complete the tally chart.

Weather	Tallies	Total Days
Sunny	~H~H~H~H ///	13
Cloudy	~H~H~H~H~H~H	
Rainy		11
Snowy		8

How many sunny days? _____

How many more rainy days than snowy days?

_____

LESSON 5·14 | **Mid-Year Assessment** *continued*

8. How much money? _____

 D N N N P P

Show 35¢. Use D, N, and P.

Part B

9. Add.

4 + 4 = _____   5   0
                        +1   +9
8 + 2 = _____   ___   ___

10. Fill in the frames.

| Rule | 80 | | | | 60 |

Find the rule. Fill in the frames.

| Rule | | 6 | 9 | | |

LESSON 5·14 | **Mid-Year Assessment** *continued*

11. Draw and solve.
There are 12 eggs in a nest.
9 eggs hatch.

How many eggs are left?

_____ eggs

Write the number model.

_____

12. How much money?

(D) (D) (N) (N) (N) (N) (P) (P)

_____¢ or $_____._____

Show the same amount using fewer coins.

LESSON 10·8 | **End-Of-Year Assessment**

Part A

1. Shade the fraction for each shape.

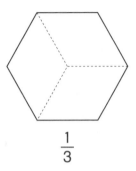
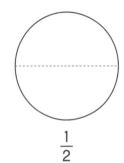
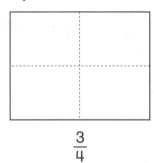

$\frac{1}{3}$ $\frac{1}{2}$ $\frac{3}{4}$

2. Use <, >, and =.

42 ☐ 24   4 + 6 ☐ 7 + 3

23 ☐ 20 + 10   78 ☐ 97

< is less than
> is more than
= is equal to

3. Use the word bank to help you write the name for each shape.

rectangle	circle	pyramid	cone	square	cube	sphere

_____   _____   _____

_____   _____   _____

LESSON 10·8 End-Of-Year Assessment *continued*

4. Add or subtract.

$3 + 3 =$ _____

$10 - 1 =$ _____

$7 +$ _____ $= 10$

_____ $= 8 - 4$

_____ $+ 0 = 17$

$0 +$ _____ $= 17$

$\begin{array}{r} 20 \\ -10 \\ \hline \end{array}$ $\qquad$ $\begin{array}{r} 16 \\ -1 \\ \hline \end{array}$ $\qquad$ $\begin{array}{r} 2 \\ -2 \\ \hline \end{array}$

5. What is your favorite flavor of ice cream?
Add your vote to the graph.

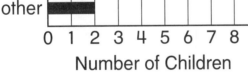

Favorite Ice Cream Flavors

Number of Children

What flavor is least

popular? _____

What flavor is most

popular? _____

How many children like vanilla ice cream? _____

6. Circle the symmetrical picture.

LESSON 10·8 End-Of-Year Assessment *continued*

7. What letter are you most likely to spin? _____

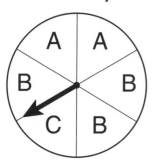

8. What is the temperature? _____ °F

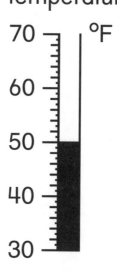

9. Measure the line segment to the nearest centimeter.

_____ about _____ cm

10. Write 3 names for 30.

30

Label the box.
Put 3 new names in the box.

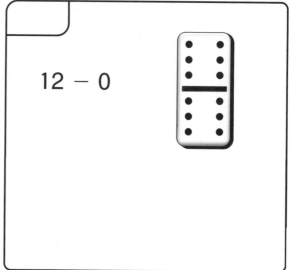

12 − 0

LESSON 10·8 **End-Of-Year Assessment** *continued*

11. Draw the hands.

4:45

quarter after 12 o'clock

12. Ⓠ Ⓠ Ⓓ Ⓓ Ⓝ Ⓝ Ⓝ Ⓟ   How much money?   _____ ¢

Show this amount with fewer coins.

13. Find the rule. Fill in the table.

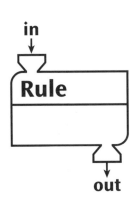

in	out
8	5
23	20
	27
52	
103	

End-Of-Year Assessment *continued*

14. Write the numbers shown by the base-10 blocks.

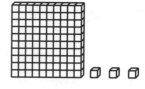

_____   _____   _____

Draw a ◯ around the ones place. Draw a △ around the tens place.

| **Part B** |

15. Cindy has $1 Ⓠ Ⓠ Ⓓ Ⓟ Ⓟ Ⓟ Ⓟ $__.___

Jacob has $1 Ⓓ Ⓓ Ⓓ Ⓓ Ⓝ Ⓝ Ⓟ Ⓟ $__.___

Who has more money? _____

How much more money? _____

16. Two people share these marbles equally.

How many marbles does each person get?

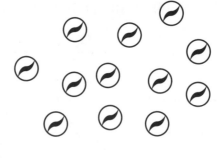

_____ marbles

17. Solve. You may use your number grid.

$$\begin{array}{r} 38 \\ -11 \\ \hline \end{array} \qquad \begin{array}{r} 67 \\ +20 \\ \hline \end{array} \qquad \begin{array}{r} 26 \\ -15 \\ \hline \end{array}$$

LESSON 10·8 **End-Of-Year Assessment** *continued*

18. Add.

$2 + 5 =$ _____ $10 + 4 =$ _____

$20 + 50 =$ _____ $20 + 4 =$ _____

$200 + 500 =$ _____ $30 + 4 =$ _____

19. Solve.
Zack found 17 shells at the beach.
Miles found 20 shells at the beach.
How many shells did Zack and Miles find in all?

_____ shells

Write a number model. _____

20. What time is it?

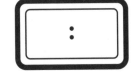

GRADE 2 | **Beginning-of-Year Assessment**

1. Measure this line segment to the nearest inch and to the nearest centimeter.

_____ inches   _____ centimeters

2. Complete the bar graph.
   Lee has 3 stickers.
   Joe has 6 stickers.
   Ivan has 4 stickers.
   Mia has 4 stickers.

   a. Maximum number of stickers:

   _____

   b. Minimum number of stickers:

   _____

   c. Median number of stickers:

   _____

   d. Mode number of stickers: _____

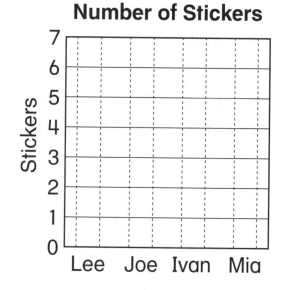

Number of Stickers

3. Color $\frac{3}{4}$.

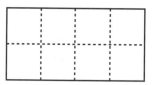

4. What fraction of the circles is shaded? _____

GRADE 2

Beginning-of-Year Assessment *cont.*

5. Shade $\frac{1}{2}$ and write the fraction.

$\frac{1}{2}$ or _____

6. Fill in the oval next to the best estimate.

a. 322 + 283 is about

    ◯ 400

    ◯ 500

    ◯ 600

b. 89 − 52 is about

    ◯ 30

    ◯ 40

    ◯ 50

7. The area of the square is _____ square centimeters.

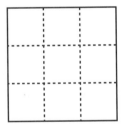

8. Use counters, a number grid, or pictures to find the answer.

Unit

a.   58
   +65
   ‾‾‾‾

b.   27
   +44
   ‾‾‾‾

c.   74
   −48
   ‾‾‾‾

d.   62
   −37
   ‾‾‾‾

Beginning-of-Year Assessment *cont.*

9. Write the time.

a.

_____ : _____

b.

_____ : _____

c.

_____ : _____

10. Complete.

1 day = _____ hours   1 week = _____ days

1 minute = _____ seconds   1 hour = _____ minutes

11. Use counters or drawings to solve.

a. 12 pencils. 4 children.

How many pencils per child? _____ pencils

b. 60 raisins. 6 raisins per child.

How many children? _____ children

12. Complete the diagram. Use counters to solve.

a. 6 bikes. Each bike has 2 wheels. How many wheels in all? _____

bikes	wheels per bike	wheels in all

GRADE 2 **Beginning-of-Year Assessment** *cont.*

b. 8 children. Each child has 2 apples.

How many apples in all? _____

children	apples per child	apples in all

13. Use =, +, or −.

a. 6 ⬜ 7 = 13

b. 12 ⬜ 2 = 10

c. 22 ⬜ 10 + 12

d. 16 = 10 ⬜ 6

e. 7 ⬜ 3 = 4

f. 30 = 50 ⬜ 20

Use bills and coins to solve.

14. Max saved $5.40 for his class field trip. His friend saved $3.50. How much money did they save in all? Write a number model.

a. Answer: _____

b. Number model: _____

15. Isabel bought 1 pen for $0.85. She paid with $1.00. How much change did Isabel get back? _____

GRADE 2

Beginning-of-Year Assessment *cont.*

16. Write the fact family for 9, 4, and 36.

_____ × _____ = _____   _____ × _____ = _____

_____ ÷ _____ = _____   _____ ÷ _____ = _____

17. Solve.

$6 \times 8 =$ _____ $8 \times 4 =$ _____

$7 \times 3 =$ _____ $7 \times 6 =$ _____

$9 \times 6 =$ _____ $9 \times 3 =$ _____

18. Solve.

a. If  is ONE, then is _____.

b. If 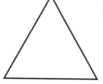 is ONE, then 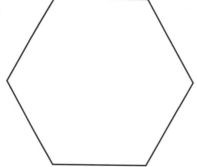 is _____.

Beginning-of-Year Assessment *cont.*

19. Kathy bought juice for $1.81. She paid with $2.00. How much change does Kathy get?

Answer: _____

20. Solve. Show your work.

a. 67	**b.** 218	**c.** 86	**d.** 115	**e.** 172
+26	+159	−37	−27	−138

21. Find the area.

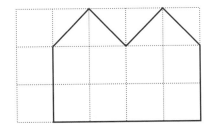

_____ square centimeters

22. Write the number that is 10,000 less and 10,000 more.

Less		**More**
	10,236	
	14,872	
	153,234	

LESSON 6·11 **Mid-Year Assessment**

Part A

1. Draw line segment $\overline{AB}$.

A •   B •

2. Circle the pair of line segments that are parallel.

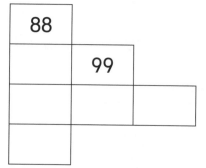

3. The temperature is

_____ °F.

4. Write the fact family for 2, 11, and 9.

_____

_____

_____

_____

5. Use <, >, or =.

462 _____ 624

209 _____ 2,009

8 + 5 _____ 7 + 5

9 + 6 _____ 8 + 7

6. Fill in the missing numbers.

88		
	99	

LESSON 6·11 **Mid-Year Assessment** *continued*

7. This shape is a

⬭ hexagon.

⬭ rhombus.

⬭ trapezoid.

8. This is a picture of a

⬭ pyramid.

⬭ cylinder.

⬭ rectangular prism.

9. Draw the hour and minute hands to show 6:45.

10. On Monday, Jen painted 30 beads for her necklace. On Tuesday, she painted 12 beads. How many beads did Jen paint in all?

a. Answer: _____

b. Number model: _____

c. Is your answer an odd or even number? _____

11. Use $1, Q, D, N, P to show two ways to make $1.25.

_____

LESSON 6·11 | **Mid-Year Assessment** *continued*

| **Part B** |

12. Fill in the Frames.

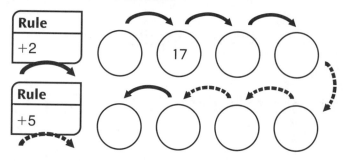

Rule +2

Rule +5

17

13. Solve. Use a number grid, base-10 blocks, or counters to help.

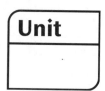

Unit

a.
$$\begin{array}{r} 34 \\ +21 \\ \hline \end{array}$$

b.
$$\begin{array}{r} 49 \\ +18 \\ \hline \end{array}$$

c.
$$\begin{array}{r} 65 \\ -43 \\ \hline \end{array}$$

d.
$$\begin{array}{r} 42 \\ -26 \\ \hline \end{array}$$

14. Solve. Draw an array or use counters.
4 rows of chairs. 5 chairs per row.
How many chairs in all?

_____ chairs

LESSON 6·11 | Mid-Year Assessment *continued*

15. Find the rule and complete the table.

Rule

in	out
$1.25	$1.00
$0.30	$0.05
	$0.75
$2.40	

16. Sally's game mat for the *Money Exchange Game* looks like this:

One Dollar $1	Ten Cents 10¢	One Cent 1¢
	(coins)	(coins)

Draw $1, Ⓓ, Ⓟ on the blank game mat to show the exchanges she can make.

One Dollar $1	Ten Cents 10¢	One Cent 1¢

Name ______________________ Date ______________ Time ______________

LESSON 12·8

End-of-Year Assessment

Part A

1. Measure this line segment to the nearest inch and to the nearest centimeter.

_______ inches _______ centimeters

2. Complete the bar graph.
Tia read 6 books.
Ian read 3 books.
Theo read 5 books.
Jen read 3 books.

a. Maximum number of books read: _______

b. Minimum number of books read: _______

c. Median number of books read: _______

d. Mode number of books read: _______

3. Color $\frac{1}{4}$.

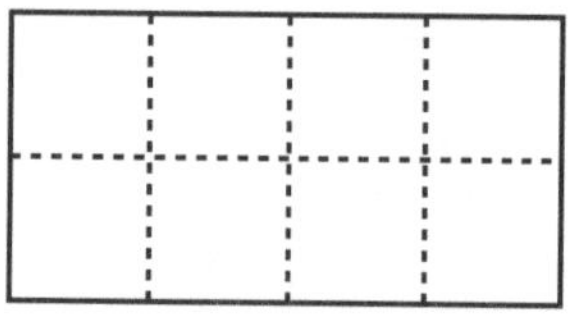

4. What fraction of the circles is shaded? _______

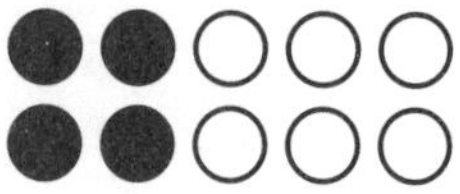

LESSON 12·8 | **End-of-Year Assessment** *continued*

5. Shade $\frac{1}{2}$ and write the fraction.

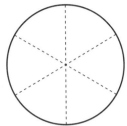

$\frac{1}{2}$ or _____

6. Fill in the oval next to the best estimate.

a. 138 + 263 is about

⊂⊃ 200

⊂⊃ 300

⊂⊃ 400

b. 92 − 59 is about

⊂⊃ 20

⊂⊃ 30

⊂⊃ 40

7. The area of the rectangle is _____ square centimeters.

8. Use counters, a number grid, or pictures to find the answer.

Unit

a. 56
     +67
     ____

b. 23
     +48
     ____

c. 72
     −46
     ____

d. 64
     −39
     ____

LESSON 12·8 End-of-Year Assessment *continued*

9. Write the time.

a.

_____ : _____

b.

_____ : _____

c.

_____ : _____

10. Complete.

1 week = _____ days   1 day = _____ hours

1 hour = _____ minutes   1 minute = _____ seconds

11. Use counters or drawings to solve.

a. 15 stickers. 3 children.

How many stickers per child? _____ stickers

b. 40 candies. 4 candies per child.

How many children? _____ children

12. Complete the diagram. Use counters to solve.

a. 5 cars. Each car has 4 wheels. How many wheels in all? _____

cars	wheels per car	wheels in all

LESSON 12·8 | **End-of-Year Assessment** *continued*

b. 6 children. Each child has 3 cookies.

How many cookies in all? _____

children	cookies per child	cookies in all

13. Use =, +, or −.

a. 8 ☐ 6 = 14

b. 15 ☐ 5 = 10

c. 25 ☐ 15 + 10

d. 18 = 10 ☐ 8

e. 9 ☐ 3 = 6

f. 20 = 40 ☐ 20

Use bills and coins to solve.

14. Ian saved $4.50 for his mother's birthday present. His sister saved $3.40. How much money did they save in all? Write a number model.

a. Answer: _____

b. Number model: _____

15. Carlos bought 1 pencil for $0.65. He paid with $1.00. How much change did Carlos get back? _____

LESSON 12·8 | **End-of-Year Assessment** *continued*

Part B

16. Write the fact family for 8, 4, and 32.

_____ × _____ = _____   _____ × _____ = _____

_____ ÷ _____ = _____   _____ ÷ _____ = _____

17. Solve.

6 × 7 = _____   8 × 6 = _____

9 × 3 = _____   7 × 4 = _____

9 × 7 = _____   6 × 6 = _____

18. Solve.

a. If 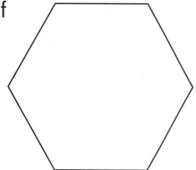 is ONE, then is _____.

b. If 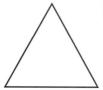 is ONE, then  is _____.

LESSON 12·8 — End-of-Year Assessment *continued*

19. Caitlin bought yogurt for $1.72. She paid with $2.00. How much change does Caitlin get?

Answer: _____

20. Solve. Show your work.

a. 65	**b.** 238	**c.** 84	**d.** 113	**e.** 154
+28	+149	−38	−25	−126

21. Find the area.

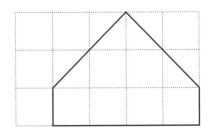

_____ square centimeters

22. Write the number that is 10,000 less and 10,000 more.

Less		More
	10,458	
	12,964	
	161,324	

GRADE 3 | **Beginning-of-Year Assessment**

1. Complete the Frames-and-Arrows problems.

a.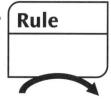

Rule
$+100$

| | | 924 | | | |

b.

Rule

150   250

2. Find the perimeter and area for this figure.

a. perimeter: _____ cm

b. area: _____ sq cm

c. Explain how you found the area.

_____

_____

3. Nikki had $9.97. How much more money does she need to buy a shirt for $14.99? Show your work.

a. Answer: _____

b. Number model: _____

GRADE 3 | **Beginning-of-Year Assessment** *cont.*

For each problem, estimate whether the sum or difference is greater than 400 or less than 400 and circle the choice that best describes your estimate. Then calculate an exact answer only to those problems with sums or differences greater than 400. Show your work.

4. a. < 400

> 400

b. 295
+185
_____

5. a. < 400

> 400

b. 206
+298
_____

6. a. < 400

> 400

b. 700
−226
_____

7. a. < 400

> 400

b. 3,106
−2,812
_____

Estimate the answer to the problem below. There is no sales tax on the items.

8. a. Alexandra wants to buy a sandwich for $3.76 and a water for $1.52. She has $5.00. Does she have enough money?

_____

How did you figure it out? Explain your thinking.

_____

_____

_____

b. Number model you used: _____

Beginning-of-Year Assessment *cont.*

9. Follow the directions for each clock.

    a. Draw the hands.   **b.** Draw the hands.   **c.** Write the time.

      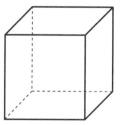

       4:35   8:12   _____:_____

10. Circle the right angle.

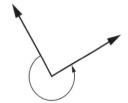   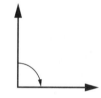   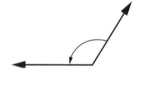

11. The picture below shows a 3-D shape. Fill in all of the ovals that describe the shape.

    ⬭ pyramid   ⬭ exactly 6 faces

    ⬭ cube   ⬭ exactly 6 edges

    ⬭ cylinder   ⬭ square bases

Beginning-of-Year Assessment *cont.*

12. Fill in the oval for the name of each shape below

a.  **b.**  **c.**  **d.**

a.	b.	c.	d.
⬭ square	⬭ trapezoid	⬭ pentagon	⬭ rhombus
⬭ hexagon	⬭ rhombus	⬭ octagon	⬭ trapezoid
⬭ rhombus	⬭ octagon	⬭ trapezoid	⬭ triangle
⬭ trapezoid	⬭ hexagon	⬭ rectangle	⬭ rectangle

13. Circle $\frac{2}{5}$ of the stars.

14. 8 children lined up for lunch. This was $\frac{1}{3}$ of the class. How many children were in the whole class?

_____
(unit)

15. Measure each line segment below to the nearest $\frac{1}{2}$ inch and to the nearest $\frac{1}{2}$ centimeter.

a. _____

about _____ inches

about _____ centimeters

b. _____

about _____ inches

about _____ centimeters

GRADE 3

Beginning-of-Year Assessment *cont.*

16. Write the fraction in each separate area. The circle represents the whole or ONE.

a.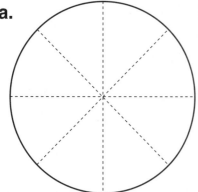

b.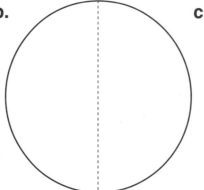

c.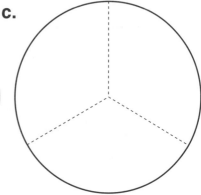

17. Marissa took a survey to find the number of times her friends went to the park in a week. She recorded the following data:

Make a bar graph to show her survey results. Remember to add labels and a title.

Number of Park Trips	Number of Children
0	////
1	ＨＨＴ /
2	ＨＨＴ
3	/
4	///
5	//

Title: _____

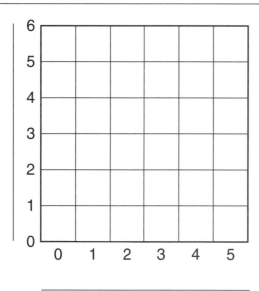

_____

18. Use the data in the tally chart and bar graph to fill in the blanks.

a. maximum _____   **c.** range _____

b. minimum _____   **d.** median _____

Beginning-of-Year Assessment *cont.*

19. Use your favorite multiplication method to solve. Show your work.

a. 62
  × 8
  ___

b. 308
  × 6
  ___

20. Juan bought 6 boxes of straws on sale. There were 9 straws in each box. How many straws did he buy altogether?

a. Answer: _____

b. Number model: _____

21. Complete the "What's My Rule?" tables and write the rules.

a.

Rule	
in	**out**
8	32
	36
20	80
25	

b.

Rule	
in	**out**
94	
60	52
	73
6	−2

c.

Rule	
in	**out**
	40
7	56
10	80
60	

GRADE 3

Beginning-of-Year Assessment *cont.*

22. Fill in the missing number in the Fact Triangle.

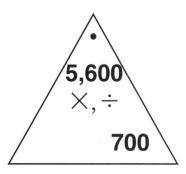

5,600
×, ÷
700

23. Write the fact family for the Fact Triangle.

_____

_____

_____

_____

24. On the top edge of the ruler below, label each mark with the letter listed.

A: $\frac{1}{4}$ in.   **B:** $3\frac{3}{8}$ in.   **C:** $1\frac{3}{4}$ in.   **D:** $4\frac{1}{8}$ in.

```
 0        1        2        3        4        5        6
Inches (in.)
```

25. How far is it from point *A* to point *C* in Problem 24? _____

26. Put in parentheses to make each number sentence true.

a. $3 \times 20 + 9 = 69$

b. $128 = 40 \times 3 + 8$

c. $60 + 40 \times 10 = 460$

d. $2,397 = 30 \times 80 - 3$

Beginning-of-Year Assessment *cont.*

27. The children in the Cooking Club baked 31 pretzels. They gave each teacher 4 pretzels. How many teachers received pretzels? How many pretzels were left over? Show your work.

a. Answer: _____

_____

b. Number model: _____

28. Solve. Use your favorite multiplication method. Show your work.

a.   17
       ×23
      ——

b.   29
       ×56
      ——

LESSON 6·13 Mid-Year Assessment

Part A

1.

a. Write the time. _____:_____

b. What time will it be in a half hour?

_____:_____

2. Fill in the oval next to the closest estimate.

a. 489 + 207 = _____

    ◯ about 500

    ◯ about 600

    ◯ about 700

b. 519 − 347 = _____

    ◯ about 150

    ◯ about 250

    ◯ about 300

Solve each problem.

3. The second grade collected 67 cans. The third grade collected 122 cans. How many cans were collected in all?

a. Answer: _____

b. Number model: _____

4. Petra had $4.75. She earned $2.50 this week. How much money does she have now?

a. Answer: _____

b. Number model:

_____

5. José had $10.00. He spent $4.85 at the toy store. How much money does he have now?

a. Answer: _____

b. Number model:

_____

LESSON 6·13 **Mid-Year Assessment** *continued*

6. 4 children
7 pencils per child
How many pencils in all?

a. _____ pencils

b. Number model: _____

children	pencils per child	pencils in all

7. 20 books shared by 4 children
How many books per child?

a. _____ books

b. Number model:

_____

children	books per child	books in all

8. Fill in the unit box. Complete each fact.

a. $7 + 8 =$ _____

b. $5 +$ _____ $= 11$

c. $6 + 7 =$ _____

d. $9 = 15 -$ _____

e. $4 +$ _____ $= 10$

f. _____ $= 9 + 7$

Unit

9. Fill in the unit box. Use $>$, $<$, or $=$.

a. 305 _____ 350

b. 160 _____ 1,006

c. 40,007 _____ 4,000.9

d. 729 _____ 927

e. 38.2 _____ 38.8

f. $300 + 400$ _____ $900 - 200$

Unit

10. Circle every digit in the tenths place in problem 9.

11. Write the smallest 6-digit number you can make with
the digits 7, 3, 4, 8, 2, and 9.

_____

LESSON 6·13 | **Mid-Year Assessment** *continued*

12. Fill in the unit box. Add or subtract. Show your work.

| **Unit** |
| |

a.
$$\begin{array}{r} 682 \\ -\ 236 \\ \hline \end{array}$$

b.
$$\begin{array}{r} 427 \\ +\ 339 \\ \hline \end{array}$$

13. Complete the Frames-and-Arrows puzzles.

a.

Rule
+10

  525 ◯ ◯ 555 ◯

b.

Rule

☐ ☐ 992 990 ☐

Part B

14. a. Draw the lines of symmetry.

   b. This polygon is called a

   _____.

Solve.

15. Ezra has 356 pennies in a jar. Jenna has 162 pennies in a box. How many more pennies does Ezra have than Jenna?

   a. Answer: _____
                           (unit)

   b. Number model: _____

LESSON 6·13 **Mid-Year Assessment** *continued*

16. Fill in the unit box. Solve each problem. Show your work.

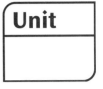
Unit

a.   2,391
      + 4,489

b.   6,704
      − 3,842

17. Write the letter for the best description of each event.

_____ A coin will land HEADS-up.   **a.** likely

_____ It will rain at least once this year.   **b.** 50-50

_____ The sun will rise tomorrow.   **c.** sure

_____ A bird will fly into your house.   **d.** unlikely

18. Find the rule and complete the table.

Rule		in	out
		3	
		2	16
		4	
			64

LESSON 11·6 End-of-Year Assessment

Part A

1. Complete the Frames-and-Arrows problems.

   a.
   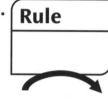
   Rule

   +100

   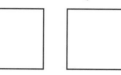

   | | | 876 | | | |

   b.
   Rule

   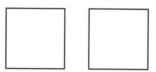

   75   125

2. Find the perimeter and area for this figure.

   a. perimeter: _____ cm

   b. area: _____ sq cm

   c. Explain how you found the area.

   _____

   _____

   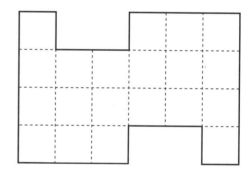

3. Natalie had $8.93. How much more money does she need to buy a CD for $11.25? Show your work.

   a. Answer: _____

   b. Number model: _____

LESSON 11·6   **End-of-Year Assessment** *continued*

For each problem, estimate whether the sum or difference is greater than 300 or less than 300 and circle the choice that best describes your estimate. Then calculate an exact answer only to those problems with sums or differences greater than 300. Show your work.

4. a. < 300

     > 300

    b.   185
        +95

5. a. < 300

     > 300

    b.   108
        +198

6. a. < 300

     > 300

    b.   600
        −128

7. a. < 300

     > 300

    b. 2,108
       −1,815

Estimate the answer to the problem below. There is no sales tax on the items.

8. a. Alejandro wants to buy a hamburger for $3.46 and a drink for $1.78. He has $5.00. Does he have enough money?

    _____

How did you figure it out? Explain your thinking.

_____

_____

_____

    b. Number model you used: _____

9. Follow the directions for each clock.

a. Draw the hands.	**b.** Draw the hands.	**c.** Write the time.
	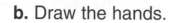	
6:55	2:42	_____ : _____

10. Circle the right angle.

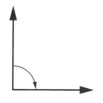  

11. The picture below shows a 3-D shape. Fill in all of the ovals that describe the shape.

⬭ pyramid   ⬭ exactly 6 faces

⬭ cube   ⬭ exactly 6 edges

⬭ prism   ⬭ rectangular bases

LESSON 11·6 | **End-of-Year Assessment** *continued*

12. Fill in the oval for the name of each shape below.

a.

  ⬭ square

  ⬭ hexagon

  ⬭ rhombus

  ⬭ trapezoid

b.

  ⬭ trapezoid

  ⬭ rhombus

  ⬭ octagon

  ⬭ hexagon

c.

  ⬭ rhombus

  ⬭ octagon

  ⬭ trapezoid

  ⬭ rectangle

d.

  ⬭ pentagon

  ⬭ trapezoid

  ⬭ triangle

  ⬭ rectangle

13. Circle $\frac{3}{5}$ of the stars.

14. 6 children lined up for gym class. This was $\frac{1}{4}$ of the class. How many children were in the whole class?

_____
                  (unit)

15. Measure each line segment below to the nearest $\frac{1}{2}$ inch and to the nearest $\frac{1}{2}$ centimeter.

  a. _____

    about _____ inches

    about _____ centimeters

  b. _____

    about _____ inches

    about _____ centimeters

End-of-Year Assessment *continued*

16. Write the fraction in each separate area. The hexagon represents the whole or ONE.

a.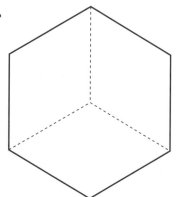

b.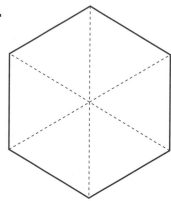

c.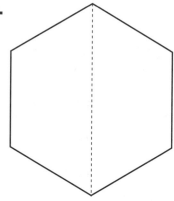

17. Serita took a survey to find the number of times her friends visited the public library in a month. She recorded the following data:

Make a bar graph to show her survey results. Remember to add labels and a title.

Number of Library Visits	Number of Children
0	//
1	////
2	HHT /
3	HHT
4	//
5	/

Title: _____

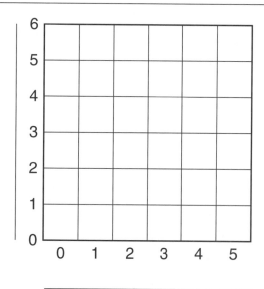

18. Use the data in the tally chart and bar graph to fill in the blanks.

a. maximum _____   **c.** range _____

b. minimum _____   **d.** median _____

LESSON 11·6 | **End-of-Year Assessment** *continued*

19. Use your favorite multiplication method to solve. Show your work.

a. 74
　　×6

b. 406
　　× 5

20. Julia bought 7 boxes of pencils on sale. There were 8 pencils in each box. How many pencils did she buy altogether?

a. Answer: _____

b. Number model: _____

21. Complete the "What's My Rule?" tables and write the rules.

a.

in	out
7	21
	24
30	90
25	

b.

Rule

in	out
82	
43	33
	65
5	−5

c.

Rule

in	out
	48
9	54
10	60
70	

LESSON 11·6 | **End-of-Year Assessment** *continued*

Part B

22. Fill in the missing number in the Fact Triangle.

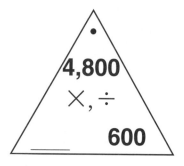

23. Write the fact family for the Fact Triangle.

_____

_____

_____

_____

24. On the top edge of the ruler below, label each mark with the letter listed.

A: $\frac{3}{4}$ in.　　　　**B:** $4\frac{7}{8}$ in.　　　　**C:** $1\frac{1}{4}$ in.　　　　**D:** $2\frac{5}{8}$ in.

```
  0       1       2       3       4       5       6
Inches (in.)
```

25. How far is it from point *A* to point *C* in Problem 24? _____

26. Put in parentheses to make each number sentence true.

　　a. $2 \times 40 + 7 = 87$　　　　　　**c.** $50 + 50 \times 10 = 550$

　　b. $124 = 60 \times 2 + 4$　　　　　**d.** $4{,}499 = 50 \times 90 - 1$

27. The children in the Garden Club picked 29 flowers. They gave each teacher 3 flowers. How many teachers received flowers? How many flowers were left over? Show your work.

a. Answer: _____

b. Number model: _____

28. Solve. Use your favorite multiplication method. Show your work.

a. 15
   $\times$21

b. 39
   $\times$58

GRADE 4 | **Beginning-of-Year Assessment**

1. Complete.

    a. $\frac{1}{4}$ of 24 = _____   **b.** 5 = $\frac{1}{4}$ of _____

    c. _____ = $\frac{5}{7}$ of 21   **d.** 12 = $\frac{3}{4}$ of _____

    e. $\frac{7}{5}$ of 25 = _____   **f.** $\frac{3}{2}$ of _____ = 21

2. Is 129 a multiple of 6? _____

    How do you know? _____

3. Is 6 a factor of 78? _____

    How do you know? _____

4. Write each fraction as a decimal and as a percent.

    a. $\frac{22}{100}$ = _____ . _____ = _____%

    b. $\frac{9}{10}$ = _____ . _____ = _____%

    c. $\frac{1}{4}$ = _____ . _____ = _____%

    d. $\frac{3}{5}$ = _____ . _____ = _____%

    e. $\frac{4}{100}$ = _____ . _____ = _____%

    f. $\frac{20}{10}$ = _____ . _____ = _____%

5. Insert >, <, or = to make each number sentence true.

    a. $\frac{3}{7}$ _____ $\frac{4}{7}$ **b.** $\frac{1}{3}$ _____ $\frac{1}{5}$ **c.** $\frac{3}{4}$ _____ $\frac{6}{7}$

    d. Explain how you solved Problem 5c.

    _____

    _____

GRADE 4

Beginning-of-Year Assessment *cont.*

6. Order the fractions from smallest to largest.

$\frac{1}{6}, \quad \frac{3}{4}, \quad \frac{1}{5}, \quad \frac{24}{25}, \quad \frac{4}{9}$ _____ _____ _____ _____ _____

  smallest   largest

7. Multiply or divide. Show your work.

a. $35 * 43 =$ _____

b. _____ $= 76 * 84$

c. _____ $= 664 / 8$

d. $748 \div 5 =$ _____

8. Add or subtract.

a. $\frac{2}{7} + \frac{3}{7} =$ _____

b. $\frac{1}{4} + \frac{2}{8} =$ _____

c. _____ $= \frac{5}{6} - \frac{1}{6}$

d. _____ $= \frac{3}{4} - \frac{1}{2}$

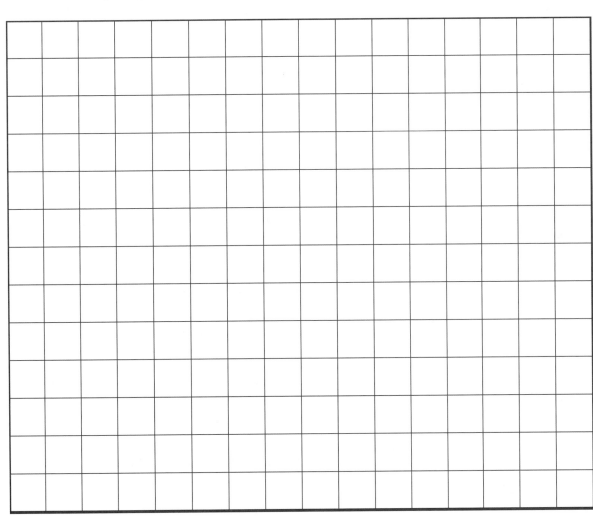

GRADE 4 Beginning-of-Year Assessment *cont.*

9. The table shows the number of people who attended a play each week during its run. Create a line graph to show the data. Use a straightedge to connect the data points. Label each axis and include a title.

Week	Number of People
1	300
2	250
3	150
4	100
5	150
6	100
7	100
8	50

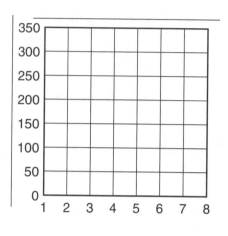

10. Use the following terms to complete the statements below.

impossible
likely
unlikely
very likely

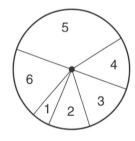

a. It is _____ that the spinner will land on 1.

b. It is _____ that the spinner will land on a number not equal to 1.

c. It is _____ that the spinner will land on a number less than $\frac{7}{8}$.

d. It is _____ that the spinner will land on a number less than or equal to 4.

GRADE 4

Beginning-of-Year Assessment *cont.*

11. Complete.

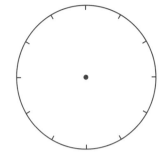

a. Color $\frac{3}{4}$ of the spinner at the right.

b. What fraction of the spinner is *not* colored? _____

c. What *percent* of the spinner is colored? _____

d. If you spin the spinner 100 times, about how many
times would you expect it to land on the colored part? _____ times

e. If you spin the spinner 400 times, about how many
times would you expect it to land on the colored part? _____ times

12. Use these formulas to calculate the areas of the figures below.

Rectangle	Parallelogram	Triangle
Area = base $*$ height	Area = base $*$ height	Area = $\frac{1}{2}$ $*$ (base $*$ height)

a.

3 in.

8 in.

Number model: _____

Area = _____

b.

6 m

9 m

Number model: _____

Area = _____

c.

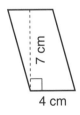

7 cm

4 cm

Number model: _____

Area = _____

Beginning-of-Year Assessment *cont.*

13. Calculate the volume of each rectangular prism.

a.

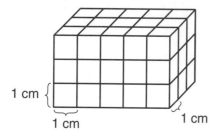

1 cm

1 cm

1 cm

Volume = _____ cm³

b.

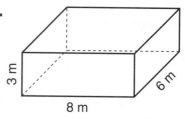

3 m

8 m

6 m

Volume = _____ m³

14. Complete.

a. 108 in. = _____ yd

b. 12 yd = _____ ft

c. 64 cm = _____ mm

d. 57 cm = _____ m

15. Complete.

a. Draw a circle at (4,1).

b. Draw a triangle at (2,5).

c. What shape is located at (5,5)? _____

d. What shape is located at (1,2)? _____

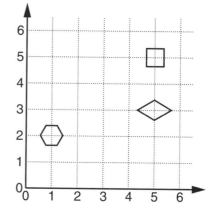

16. Estimate the measure of each angle. Do not use a protractor.

a.

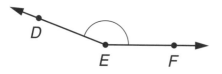

D

E   F

∠*DEF* is an _____
(acute or obtuse) angle.

∠*DEF* measures about _____ °.

b.

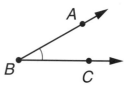

A

B

C

∠*ABC* is an _____
(acute or obtuse) angle.

∠*ABC* measures about _____ °.

GRADE 4

Beginning-of-Year Assessment *cont.*

17. The objects below have the shapes of geometric solids. Name the solids.

a. _____   **b.** _____

18. Label each figure as a *reflection, rotation,* or *translation* of the original figure. Use each word one time only.

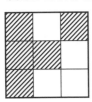   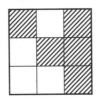

original   _____   _____   _____

19. Complete the pattern and describe the rule.

Rule: _____

5, 95, 185, 275, 365, _____, _____, _____

20. Insert parentheses to make each number sentence true.

a. 140 − 80 + 40 = 20

b. 180 = 180 − 90 * 2

c. 160 = 320 ÷ 80 ÷ 40

d. 26 + 10 ÷ 3 * 4 = 3

GRADE 4

Beginning-of-Year Assessment *cont.*

21. Complete.

    a. 25% of 28 = _____   **b.** 40% of 60 = _____   **c.** 250% of 12 = _____

22. Write each fraction as a decimal and as a percent.

    a. $\frac{19}{20}$ = _____ . _____ = _____%

    b. $\frac{2}{3}$ = _____ . _____ = _____%

    c. $\frac{12}{16}$ = _____ . _____ = _____%

    d. $\frac{2}{50}$ = _____ . _____ = _____%

23. Insert $>$, $<$, or $=$ to make each number sentence true.

    a. $-\frac{2}{3}$ _____ $-\frac{1}{3}$ **b.** $-\frac{4}{8}$ _____ $-\frac{1}{4}$

    c. -16.2 _____ -14.6 **d.** -0.8 _____ $-\frac{4}{5}$

24. Multiply and divide. Show your work.

    a. _____ = 7.3 ∗ 3.5   **b.** 228.6 / 6 = _____

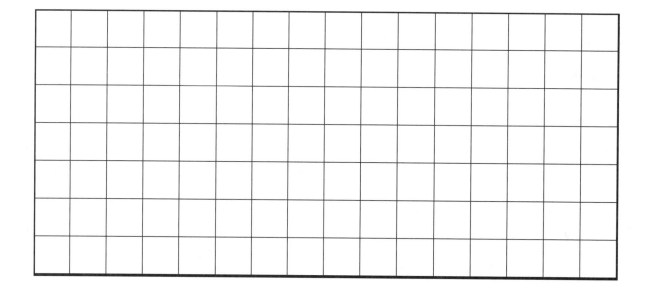

Beginning-of-Year Assessment *cont.*

25. Estimate. Is the sum or difference closest to 0, 1, or 2?

a. $\frac{1}{7} + \frac{1}{6}$ _____

b. $\frac{1}{3} + \frac{3}{4}$ _____

c. $3\frac{3}{14} - \frac{7}{8}$ _____

d. $\frac{9}{10} - \frac{6}{7}$ _____

26. Use your protractor. Measure each angle below to the nearest degree.

a.

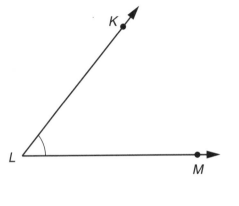

b.

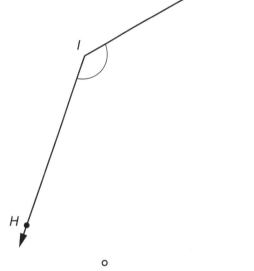

$\angle KLM$ measures _____ ° .

$\angle HIJ$ measures _____ ° .

27. Takako surveyed the students in her class to find out which fresh fruits they like best.
Use the circle graph to answer the questions below.

a. What is the most favorite fresh fruit?

b. Do more students like strawberries
or grapes? _____

c. Which fruit is less popular than strawberries?

_____

Favorite Fresh Fruit

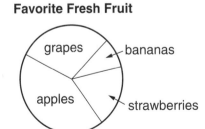

LESSON 6·11 Mid-Year Assessment

Copyright © Wright Group/McGraw-Hill

Part A

1. Write each number with digits.

a. Twelve thousand, five hundred sixty-five _____

b. Four million, six hundred thousand, twenty-seven _____

c. Twelve and four-tenths _____

d. Five and sixteen-hundredths _____

2. List the factor pairs of 32.

_____ and _____

_____ and _____

_____ and _____

3. Name the first 10 multiples of 9.

_____ _____ _____ _____ _____

_____ _____ _____ _____ _____

4. Nishi wanted to show the number 54 on her calculator. The 4-key on her calculator was broken, so this is what she did: 108 ÷ 2 =

Find two other ways to show 54 without using the 4-key. Try to use different numbers and operations.

a. _____

b. _____

Complete the "What's My Rule?" tables and state the rules.

5. Rule: _____

in	out
600	1,500
	1,200
400	
1,200	2,100
800	

6. Rule: _____

in	out
700	4,200
	1,200
50	
8,000	4,800
	2,400

LESSON 6·11 | **Mid-Year Assessment** *continued*

Solve. Use paper-and-pencil algorithms.

7. A gallon of skim milk costs $3.09 at the Gem supermarket and $4.19 at the 6-to-Midnight convenience store. How much more does a gallon of milk cost at the convenience store?

$ _____

8. Keena bought some supplies for school. The crayons cost $1.29, the notebooks cost $2.49, and the pencils cost $0.89. How much did Keena spend in all?

$ _____

9. _____ = 3,551 + 2,279

10. 2,653 − 1,289 = _____

11. 7 * 128 = _____

12. _____ = 385 / 7

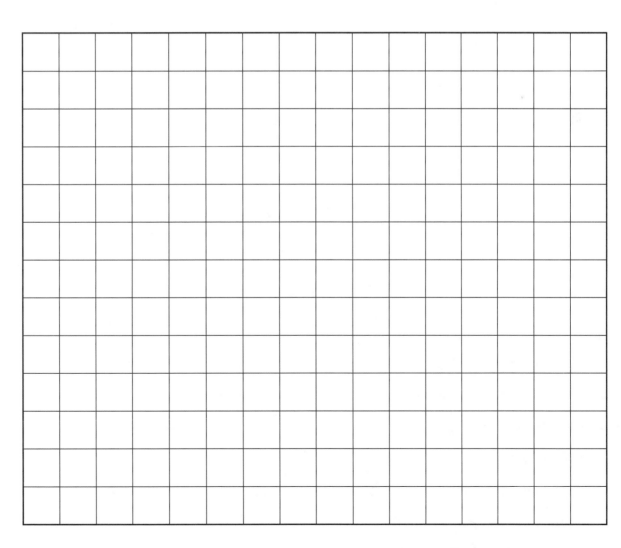

Mid-Year Assessment *continued*

13. A farm stand sells apples. The farmer records how many pounds of each type of apple are sold per day. Below are the results of Monday's sales:

18 Red Delicious   25 Gala   24 Fuji

21 Granny Smith   17 Empire   14 Pink Lady

Create a bar graph using the data above. Include labels and a title.

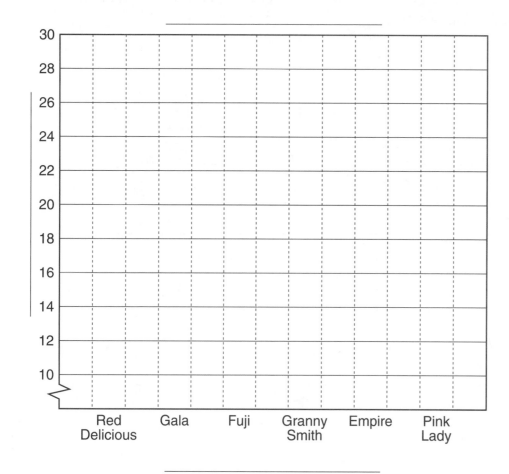

14. As part of her science project on sleep, Ama asked 13 students in her class how many hours, to the nearest half-hour, they had slept the night before. Here are the results of her survey:

Number of hours of sleep: 7, 10.5, 8, 8, 9, 10, 10, 7.5, 9.5, 9, 8, 8.5, 8

  a. What is the median number of hours the students slept? _____

  b. What is the mode? _____

  c. What is the minimum number of hours slept? _____

  d. What is the maximum number of hours slept? _____

  e. What is the range of hours they slept? _____

LESSON 6·11 | **Mid-Year Assessment** *continued*

15. Measure the line segment to the nearest inch.

_____

_____ in.

16. Measure the line segment to the nearest $\frac{1}{2}$ inch.

_____

_____ in.

17. Measure the line segment to the nearest $\frac{1}{4}$ inch.

_____

_____ in.

18. Measure the line segment to the nearest centimeter.

_____

_____ cm

19. Measure the line segment to the nearest half-centimeter.

_____

_____ cm

20. Draw $\overrightarrow{QR}$ parallel to $\overleftrightarrow{ST}$. Draw line segment *WX* so that it intersects ray *QR* and line *ST*.

LESSON 6·11   Mid-Year Assessment *continued*

Use your Geometry Template to complete Problems 21–24.

21. Draw a quadrangle that has two pairs of parallel sides and is not a square.

22. Draw a regular polygon.

What kind of quadrangle is this?

_____

Name the polygon.

_____

23. Draw a trapezoid.

24. Draw a shape that is not a polygon.

How many pairs of parallel sides does it have? _____

The shape is not a polygon because

_____

_____

25. Find the solution of each open sentence.

    a. $32 = x * 8$ Solution: _____

    b. $7 * y = 42$ Solution: _____

    c. $m / 9 = 5$ Solution: _____

    d. $54 / s = 6$ Solution: _____

26. Tell whether each number sentence is true or false.

    a. $(5 * 6) + 13 = 43$ _____

    b. $(81 / 9) - (36 / 4) = 3$ _____

    c. $30 - (4 * 7) = 2$ _____

    d. $(12 - 6) * 32 = 36$ _____

LESSON 6·11 | **Mid-Year Assessment** *continued*

Part B

27. Insert >, <, or = to make each number sentence true.

    a. 10^3 _____ 10,000   **b.** 10^6 _____ 1,000,000   **c.** 1,000 _____ 10^2

28. Rename each decimal as a fraction.

    a. 0.2 = _____   **b.** 0.75 = _____   **c.** 0.84 = _____

Solve. Use a paper-and-pencil algorithm.

29. 49 * 67 = _____	**30.** _____ = 251 * 35	**31.** 786 / 24 = _____

32. Landon picked 5 different number cards from a deck numbered 0–18. He did not pick a 7. The mean of the 5 cards is 7. Name 5 cards that Landon might have picked.

    _____   _____   _____   _____   _____

33. Complete.

    a. 1.5 m = _____ cm   **b.** 56 cm = _____ mm

    c. 0.2 m = _____ cm   **d.** 0.8 m = _____ mm

LESSON 12·7

End-of-Year Assessment

Part A

1. Complete.

a. $\frac{1}{8}$ of 24 = _____

b. 3 = $\frac{1}{4}$ of _____

c. _____ = $\frac{4}{7}$ of 14

d. 10 = $\frac{2}{3}$ of _____

e. $\frac{6}{5}$ of 20 = _____

f. $\frac{4}{3}$ of _____ = 24

2. Is 127 a multiple of 7? _____

How do you know? _____

3. Is 4 a factor of 88? _____

How do you know? _____

4. Write each fraction as a decimal and as a percent.

a. $\frac{34}{100}$ = _____ . _____ = _____%

b. $\frac{7}{10}$ = _____ . _____ = _____%

c. $\frac{3}{4}$ = _____ . _____ = _____%

d. $\frac{4}{5}$ = _____ . _____ = _____%

e. $\frac{2}{100}$ = _____ . _____ = _____%

f. $\frac{15}{10}$ = _____ . _____ = _____%

5. Insert >, <, or = to make each number sentence true.

a. $\frac{3}{5}$ _____ $\frac{2}{5}$

b. $\frac{1}{4}$ _____ $\frac{1}{6}$

c. $\frac{2}{3}$ _____ $\frac{9}{10}$

d. Explain how you solved Problem 5c.

_____

_____

LESSON 12·7   **End-of-Year Assessment** *continued*

6. Order the fractions from smallest to largest.

$\frac{5}{6}$, $\frac{1}{3}$, $\frac{1}{10}$, $\frac{19}{20}$, $\frac{2}{5}$ _____   _____   _____   _____   _____

smallest   largest

7. Multiply or divide. Show your work.

   a. $45 * 23 =$ _____   b. _____ $= 86 * 74$

   c. _____ $= 486 / 6$ d. $895 \div 7 =$ _____

8. Add or subtract.

   a. $\frac{1}{5} + \frac{3}{5} =$ _____   b. $\frac{1}{3} + \frac{3}{6} =$ _____

   c. _____ $= \frac{3}{4} - \frac{1}{4}$ d. _____ $= \frac{7}{8} - \frac{1}{2}$

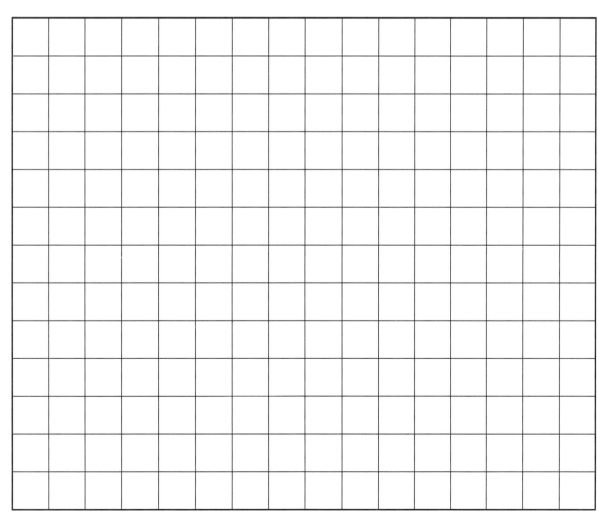

LESSON 12·7 | **End-of-Year Assessment** *continued*

9. The table shows the number of people who attended lacrosse games each week during the spring season. Create a line graph to show the data. Use a straightedge to connect the data points. Label each axis and include a title.

Week	Number of People
1	60
2	80
3	40
4	100
5	100
6	80
7	120
8	110

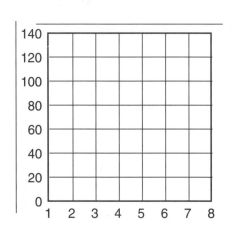

10. Use the following terms to complete the statements below.

impossible
likely
unlikely
very likely

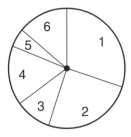

a. It is _____ that the spinner will land on a number less than or equal to 2.

b. It is _____ that the spinner will land on a number not equal to 5.

c. It is _____ that the spinner will land on a number less than $\frac{9}{10}$.

d. It is _____ that the spinner will land on 5.

LESSON 12·7

End-of-Year Assessment *continued*

11. Complete.

   a. Color $\frac{1}{4}$ of the spinner at the right.

   b. What fraction of the spinner is *not* colored? _____

   c. What *percent* of the spinner is colored? _____

   d. If you spin the spinner 100 times, about how many
      times would you expect it to land on the colored part? _____ times

   e. If you spin the spinner 300 times, about how many
      times would you expect it to land on the colored part? _____ times

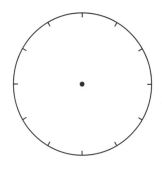

12. Use these formulas to calculate the areas of the figures below.

Rectangle	Parallelogram	Triangle
Area = base * height	Area = base * height	Area = $\frac{1}{2}$ * (base * height)

   a.

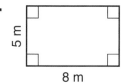

Number model: _____

Area = _____

   b.

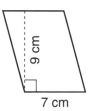

Number model: _____

Area = _____

   c.

Number model: _____

Area = _____

LESSON 12·7

End-of-Year Assessment *continued*

13. Calculate the volume of each rectangular prism.

a.

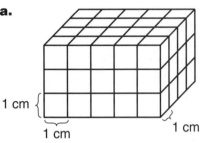

1 cm

1 cm   1 cm

Volume = _____ cm³

b.

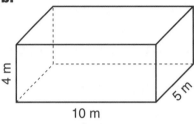

4 m

10 m

5 m

Volume = _____ m³

14. Complete.

a. 72 in. = _____ yd

b. 10 yd = _____ ft

c. 56 cm = _____ mm

d. 63 cm = _____ m

15. Complete.

a. Draw a triangle at (5,4).

b. Draw a square at (1,5).

c. What shape is located at (2,3)? _____

d. What shape is located at (3,2)? _____

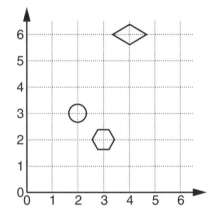

16. Estimate the measure of each angle. Do not use a protractor.

a.

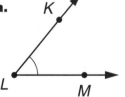

K

L   M

∠*KLM* is an _____
(acute or obtuse) angle.

∠*KLM* measures about _____ °.

b.

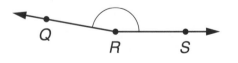

Q   R   S

∠*QRS* is an _____
(acute or obtuse) angle.

∠*QRS* measures about _____ °.

End-of-Year Assessment *continued*

17. The objects below have the shapes of geometric solids. Name the solids.

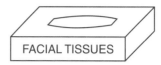

a. _____   **b.** _____

18. Label each figure as a *reflection, rotation,* or *translation* of the original figure. Use each word one time only.

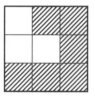

original   _____   _____   _____

19. Complete the pattern and describe the rule.

Rule: _____

5, 75, 145, 215, 285, _____, _____, _____

20. Insert parentheses to make each number sentence true.

a. $120 - 60 + 20 = 40$

b. $160 = 160 - 80 * 2$

c. $90 = 270 \div 90 \div 30$

d. $14 + 10 \div 2 * 6 = 2$

LESSON 12·7

End-of-Year Assessment *continued*

Part B

21. Complete.

a. 25% of 24 = _____   **b.** 30% of 50 = _____   **c.** 150% of 14 = _____

22. Write each fraction as a decimal and as a percent.

a. $\frac{17}{20}$ = _____ . _____ = _____%

b. $\frac{1}{3}$ = _____ . _____ = _____%

c. $\frac{4}{16}$ = _____ . _____ = _____%

d. $\frac{3}{50}$ = _____ . _____ = _____%

23. Insert >, <, or = to make each number sentence true.

a. $-\frac{1}{4}$ _____ $-\frac{3}{4}$ **b.** $-\frac{4}{10}$ _____ $-\frac{4}{5}$

c. -14.6 _____ -12.8 **d.** -0.6 _____ $-\frac{3}{5}$

24. Multiply and divide. Show your work.

a. _____ = 4.5 * 6.9   **b.** 212.4 / 9 = _____

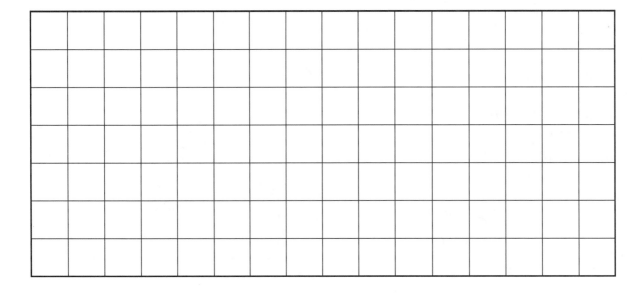

LESSON 12·7 **End-of-Year Assessment** *continued*

25. Estimate. Is the sum or difference closest to 0, 1, or 2?

  a. $\frac{1}{5} + \frac{1}{8}$ _____

  b. $1\frac{2}{3} + \frac{1}{2}$ _____

  c. $2\frac{1}{12} - \frac{9}{10}$ _____

  d. $\frac{7}{8} - \frac{5}{6}$ _____

26. Use your protractor. Measure each angle below to the nearest degree.

  a.

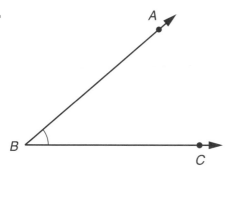

  b.

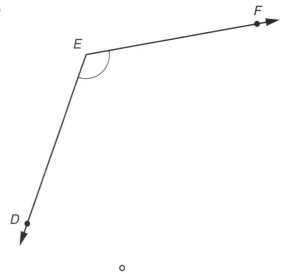

$\angle ABC$ measures _____ °. $\angle DEF$ measures _____ °.

27. Austin surveyed the students in his class to find out which breakfast drinks they like best.
Use the circle graph to answer the questions below.

  a. What is the least favorite breakfast drink?

    _____

  b. Do more students like cranberry juice or water? _____

  c. Which drink is more popular than milk?

    _____

Favorite Breakfast Drink

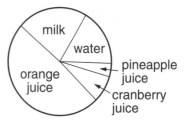

GRADE 5 Beginning-of-Year Assessment

1. A figure is partly hidden. Which of the following might it be? (Circle all possible answers.)

rectangle

triangle

trapezoid

square

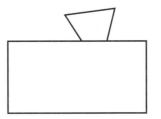

2. Add two numbers to the data set below so that

- the median of the new data set is 9,
- the maximum is 17, and
- the range is 14.

8   15   6   11   9   _____   _____

3. Write the following numbers in expanded notation.

a. 3,049 = _____

b. 56.25 = _____

4. A package of party favors contains 10 favors. Mr. Thomas is expecting 42 people at his party. He wants to have enough party favors for each person to have 2. How many

packages of favors should he buy? _____

5. A ribbon is $8\frac{1}{4}$ inches long. If you cut off $\frac{3}{8}$ of an inch, how much is left? _____ inches

6. Sean combined $\frac{2}{3}$ cup of cheddar cheese with $\frac{1}{4}$ cup of American cheese.

Is the total cheese more or less than 1 cup? _____

Explain. _____

_____

GRADE 5

Beginning-of-Year Assessment

7. Complete the table.

Standard Notation	Exponential Notation	Repeated-Factor Notation
	2^5	
10,000		
		7*7*7

Each square in the grid below has an area of 1 square centimeter.

8. What is the area of triangle *TOP*? _____ cm²

9. Draw a rectangle that has an area of 14 cm².

10. What is the perimeter of this rectangle? _____ cm

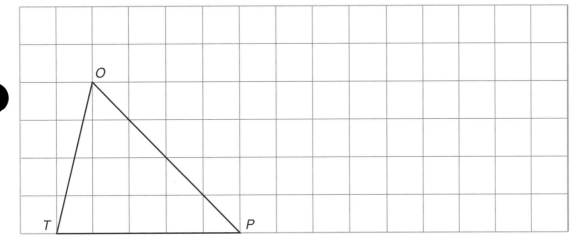

11. Insert parentheses to make the number sentences true.

$120 \div 4 * 3 + 7 = 300$ $180 = 37 - 8 + 16 * 4$

12. Kelsey said that she could use just the numbers 12, 3, and 36 to write four true

number sentences. Is Kelsey correct? _____ Why or why not?

_____

_____

_____

_____

GRADE 5 Beginning-of-Year Assessment

13. Circle the equivalent numbers.

$\frac{4}{20}$ 0.2   80% $\frac{1}{5}$ $\frac{38}{40}$ $\frac{15}{16}$ 20%

Use >, <, or = .

14. $\frac{3}{5}$ _____ $\frac{3}{6}$ **15.** $2\frac{2}{3}$ _____ $\frac{25}{12}$ **16.** $\frac{3}{9}$ _____ 0.33

17. Plot the ordered pairs on the grid. Connect the points in the same order they were plotted. (1,9); (3,9); (4,9); (7,9); (9,9); (7,7); (5,7); (3,7); (2,8); (1,9)

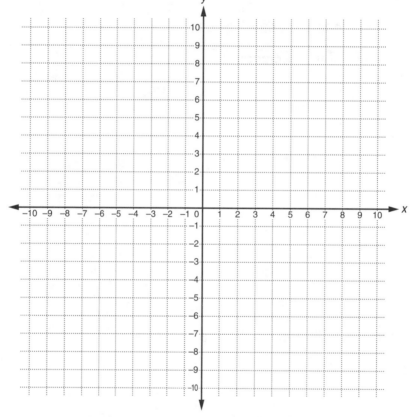

18. Describe how the figure would change…

a. if the first number of each original pair was changed to the opposite number.

_____

_____

b. if the second number of each original pair was changed to the opposite number.

_____

_____

GRADE 5 Beginning-of-Year Assessment

19. Write the 8-digit number that has a 6 in the tens place, a 2 in the hundredths place, an 8 in the hundred-thousands place, and a 1 in all the other places.

____ ____ ____, ____ ____ ____ . ____ ____

20. What is the probability of drawing a jack of diamonds from a regular deck of 52 cards? _____

21. What is the probability of drawing a 9 from a regular deck of 52 cards? _____

22. Measure the angles below.

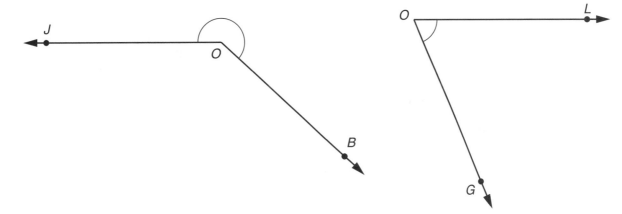

∠*JOB* measures about _____.   ∠*GOL* measures about _____.

23. Circle the acute angle in Problem 22.

What type of angle is the other angle? _____

Solve. Do not use a calculator.

24. 553 ÷ 7 = _____   **25.** 204 * 38 = _____   **26.** 264 ÷ 11 = _____

27. 6.47 * 26 = _____   **28.** 86.4 / 4 = _____   **29.** 28.2 * 6.2 = _____

30. $2\frac{1}{4} + 4\frac{1}{2} =$ _____   **31.** $3\frac{1}{6} - \frac{9}{8} =$ _____   **32.** $2\frac{3}{9} + \frac{5}{6} =$ _____

GRADE 5 **Beginning-of-Year Assessment**

33. Mark the following points on the ruler.

   A: $\frac{1}{8}$ *B:* $2\frac{1}{4}$ *C:* $1\frac{3}{16}$ *D:* $2\frac{13}{16}$ *E:* $\frac{12}{8}$

34. Write the prime factorization for 290. _____

Write each fraction in its simplest form.

35. $\frac{37}{4} =$ _____ **36.** $5\frac{12}{32} =$ _____ **37.** $\frac{50}{7} =$ _____

38. $\frac{60}{5} =$ _____ **39.** $4\frac{12}{36} =$ _____ **40.** $16\frac{60}{75} =$ _____

41. If $\frac{5}{6}$ of a set is 20, how many are in the whole set? _____

   Explain your solution strategy. _____

   _____

Write $>$, $<$, or $=$.

42. -4 _____ 4 **43.** -20 _____ -15 **44.** -0.25 _____ -0.5

45. $-5 + 5$ _____ 0 **46.** $-3 - (-6)$ _____ $4 + (-7)$ **47.** $15 + (-5)$ _____ $10 + 10$

48. Circle the number sentences that are true.

   $5 + (7 * 4) = 40$ $36 = 2^2 + 3 * 7$ $30 / (2 + 8 + 5) = 2$

   $0 = (-5 + 3) * 2$ $37 - 15 / 5 + 8 = 42$ $18 / 3 + 3 * 4 = 18$

GRADE 5

Beginning-of-Year Assessment

49. Write an open number sentence. Then solve the problem.

Claudia was cleaning her collection of seashells. She had already cleaned 28 of them. If that was $\frac{7}{8}$ of them, how many did she have left to clean?

Open sentence: _____

Answer: _____

Explain: _____

_____

50. Complete the table. Then graph the data in the table.

Rule: Number of miles = days * 36 miles

Time (days)	Number of miles
1	
4	144
3	
	72
	126

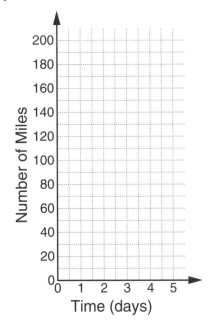

51. What is the volume of the prism to the right?

_____
(unit)

4 in.

5 in.   3 in.

Volume of a prism: $V = B * h$

52. A cylindrical can has a base with an area of 16.4 square centimeters. It has a height of 10 centimeters.

What is its volume? _____
(unit)

Volume of a cylinder: $V = B * h$

Beginning-of-Year Assessment

Find the missing number.

53. $\frac{1}{3} = \frac{17}{x}$ $x =$ _____

54. $\frac{10}{16} = \frac{s}{8}$ $s =$ _____

55. $\frac{n}{200} = \frac{2}{5}$ $n =$ _____

56. $\frac{45}{m} = \frac{5}{8}$ $m =$ _____

Complete the table.

	Exponential Notation	Standard Notation	Number-and-Word Notation
57.	$2 * 10^4$		
58.		9,000,000	
59.			3.7 hundred-million
60.	$4.6 * 10^9$		

61. Shorts sell for $15.00 each. With a shopper's card, the price is discounted 20%. There is an additional 10% off the discounted total cost if you buy two or more pairs. What is the discounted cost of 3 pairs of shorts? Show your work on the back of this page.

Discounted cost: _____

Find the greatest common factor for each pair of numbers below.

62. 32 and 80 _____

63. 80 and 20 _____

Find the least common multiple for each pair of numbers below.

64. 5 and 10 _____

65. 4 and 10 _____

GRADE 5

Beginning-of-Year Assessment *cont.*

66. Circle the figure below that has the greatest volume.

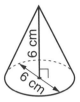

cone

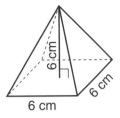

square pyramid

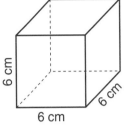

cube

Volume of a cone: $V = \frac{1}{3} * (B * h)$

Volume of a pyramid: $V = \frac{1}{3} * (B * h)$

Volume of a prism: $V = B * h$

Explain. _____

_____

_____

_____

Solve. Write your answers in simplest form.

67. a. $\frac{6}{7} * \frac{12}{14} =$ _____   **b.** $10\frac{3}{4} * \frac{4}{6} =$ _____   **c.** $4\frac{2}{7} * 3\frac{3}{5} =$ _____

68. a. $\frac{5}{6} \div \frac{1}{12} =$ _____   **b.** $11\frac{2}{3} \div 9\frac{5}{6} =$ _____   **c.** $\frac{1}{4} \div \frac{7}{8} =$ _____

LESSON 6·11 — Mid-Year Assessment

Solve the problems below. Show your work.

1. $28 * 9 =$ _____

2. $47 * 68 =$ _____

3. $235 * 56 =$ _____

4. $715 + 308 =$ _____

5. $9.43 + 7.6 =$ _____

6. $51.2 + 17.6 =$ _____

7. $247 - 196 =$ _____

8. $50.3 - 27.6 =$ _____

9. $80.3 - 5.17 =$ _____

Solve for y. Show your work.

10. $15 - y = 9$ _____

11. $8 * y = 72$ _____

12. $150 / y = 30$ _____

13. Circle all the numbers below that are factors of 48.

> 2   4   5   6   12   14   20   24

Evelyn timed how many minutes it took her to travel to work on nine different days. Find the landmarks for her data.

45   42   45   55   48   50   35   58   44

14. Median: _____ minutes

15. Maximum: _____ minutes

16. Minimum: _____ minutes

17. Range: _____ minutes

LESSON 6·11 **Mid-Year Assessment** *continued*

18. If you were Evelyn, how much time would you
allow for travel to work based on the data landmarks? _____

19. Explain your answer to Problem 18.

_____

_____

_____

20. Circle all the numbers below that are greater than $\frac{1}{2}$.

$\frac{1}{4}$ $\frac{9}{10}$ 0.66 $\frac{5}{20}$ $\frac{4}{8}$ 0.09

21. Jianhua buys a carton of milk for 59 cents, a hamburger for $1.25, and a
salad for $1.50. He pays with a five-dollar bill.

How much did he spend? _____

How much change should he get? _____

22. Name a number between 400 and 500 that is divisible by 3 but not by 2. _____

Explain how you found your number.

_____

_____

_____

_____

23. Is 71 prime or composite? _____

Explain how you found your number.

_____

_____

_____

LESSON 6·11 Mid-Year Assessment *continued*

24. Circle all the expressions below that are equivalent to $\frac{3}{4}$.

0.75 $\frac{8}{6}$ $\frac{6}{12}$ $\frac{9}{16}$ $\frac{15}{20}$ 34%

25. Write the 8-digit number that has a 4 in the hundreds place, a 5 in the thousandths place, a 9 in the ten-thousands place, and 1s in all other places.

____ ____ , ____ ____ ____ . ____ ____ ____

Add. Use the fraction sticks to help.

26. $\frac{1}{2} + \frac{1}{4} =$ _____

27. $\frac{3}{8} + \frac{1}{4} =$ _____

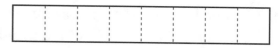

28. $\frac{3}{4} + \frac{3}{4} =$ _____

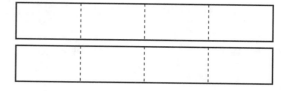

29. $\frac{1}{8} + \frac{1}{2} =$ _____

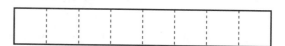

30. Explain the errors in the problem.

```
    24
  * 96
    18      _____
   360      _____
    12      _____
   240      _____
   630      _____
```

Mid-Year Assessment *continued*

31. Make a magnitude estimate for the product in Problem 30. Circle the appropriate box.

10s	100s	1,000s	10,000s

Simeon was writing a report on trees in his town. He counted the different types of trees in his neighborhood and made a circle graph. Use his circle graph to answer these questions:

32. What was the most common type of tree? _____

33. Which types of trees made up one-fourth or more of the sample?

_____

34. If there were a total of 200 trees in his sample, how many would be oaks? _____

Explain how you got your answer.

_____

_____

_____

_____

_____

_____

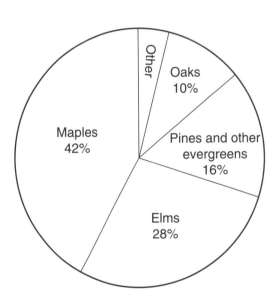

LESSON 6·11 **Mid-Year Assessment** *continued*

Part B

35. Laquita wrote 2 * 2 * 3 * 5 for the prime factorization of 48. Explain why you agree or disagree with her answer.

_____

_____

36. Draw and label a rectangle that has a base of 6.5 cm and a height of 4 cm. Use your ruler or any other tool that you wish.

37. Find the perimeter of the rectangle you drew.

Perimeter: _____
   (unit)

38. Measure each angle below. Record your answer to the nearest degree.

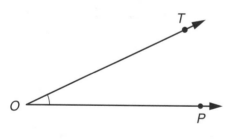

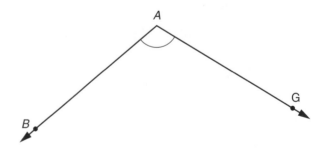

∠*TOP* measures about _____.

∠*BAG* measures about _____.

39. Circle the obtuse angle in Problem 38.

LESSON 6·11 **Mid-Year Assessment** *continued*

40. Plot the following points on the grid to the right. Connect the points.

(2,1); (3,3); (5,1); (6,3)

41. What shape did you draw in Problem 40?

_____

42. Give two other names for the shape you drew in Problem 40.

_____   _____

43. Write these numerals in expanded notation.

a. 123.576 _____

b. 6,788,392 _____

44. Nadine baby-sits for her neighbor and is paid once a month. She earned $94.75 in January. Her neighbor asked if she would like to be paid the exact amount, or have the amount rounded to the nearest tenth, ten, or hundred of a dollar. Which option should Nadine take? Explain your reasoning.

_____

_____

_____

45. Write the following fractions and mixed numbers in simplest form.

a. $\frac{9}{12}$ _____   **b.** $\frac{49}{7}$ _____   **c.** $6\frac{16}{4}$ _____   **d.** $3\frac{6}{8}$ _____

LESSON 12·9   **End-of-Year Assessment**

Part A

1. A figure is partly hidden. Which of the following might it be? (Circle all possible answers.)

   rectangle

   triangle

   trapezoid

   square

   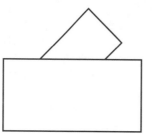

2. Add two numbers to the data set below so that

   • the median of the new data set is 5,
   • the maximum is 15, and
   • the range is 13.

   4   5   4   11   8   _____   _____

3. Write the following numbers in expanded notation.

   a. 2,096 = _____

   b. 38.75 = _____

4. A package of hot dog buns contains 12 buns. Mrs. Hudson is expecting 35 people at her picnic. She wants to have enough hot dog buns for each person to have 2. How many packages of buns should she buy? _____

5. A board is $6\frac{1}{8}$ inches long. If you cut off $\frac{3}{4}$ of an inch, how much is left? _____ inches

6. Jean combined $\frac{1}{3}$ cup of corn flour with $\frac{3}{4}$ cup of white flour. Is the total flour more or less than 1 cup? _____

   Explain. _____

   _____

LESSON 12·9 **End-of-Year Assessment** *continued*

7. Complete the table.

Standard Notation	Exponential Notation	Repeated-Factor Notation
	3^6	
1,000		
		9 * 9 * 9

Each square in the grid below has an area of 1 square centimeter.

8. What is the area of triangle *END*? _____ cm^2

9. Draw a rectangle that has an area of 12 cm^2.

10. What is the perimeter of this rectangle? _____ cm

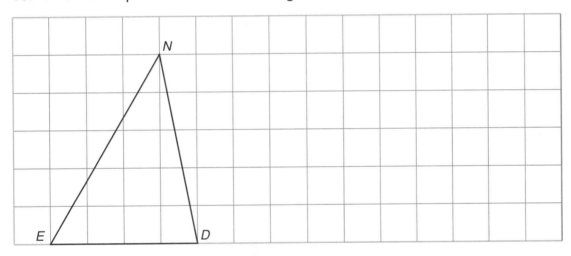

11. Insert parentheses to make the number sentences true.

210 ÷ 6 * 2 + 5 = 5   144 = 18 − 12 + 42 * 3

12. Ivan said that he could use just the numbers 18, 3, and 36 to write four true

number sentences. Is Ivan correct? _____ Why or why not?

_____

_____

_____

_____

_____

LESSON 12·9 | **End-of-Year Assessment** *continued*

13. Circle the equivalent numbers.

$\frac{19}{20}$ 0.95   19% $\frac{1}{5}$ $\frac{38}{40}$ $\frac{15}{16}$ 95%

Use >, <, or = .

14. $\frac{3}{8}$ _____ $\frac{3}{7}$ **15.** $3\frac{2}{3}$ _____ $\frac{24}{10}$ **16.** $\frac{5}{15}$ _____ 0.66

17. Plot the ordered pairs on the grid. Connect the points in the same order they were plotted. (1,1); (4,1); (6,1); (9,1); (8,3); (7,5); (5,5); (3,5); (2,3);

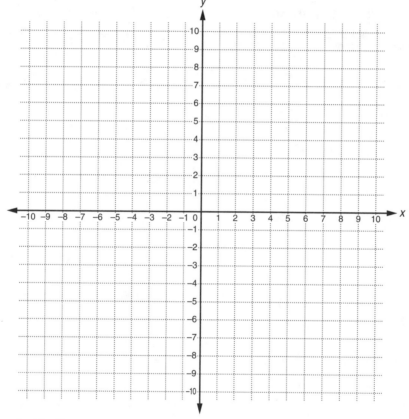

18. Add a point at (6,3). Then describe how the figure would change…

a. if the first number of each original pair was changed to the opposite number.

_____

_____

b. if the second number of each original pair was changed to the opposite number.

_____

_____

LESSON 12·9 End-of-Year Assessment *continued*

19. Write the 8-digit number that has a 5 in the tens place, a 3 in the hundredths place, a 4 in the hundred-thousands place, and 8 in all the other places.

____ ____ ____ , ____ ____ ____ . ____ ____

20. What is the probability of drawing a king of hearts from a regular deck of 52 cards? _____

21. What is the probability of drawing a 5 from a regular deck of 52 cards? _____

22. Measure the angles below.

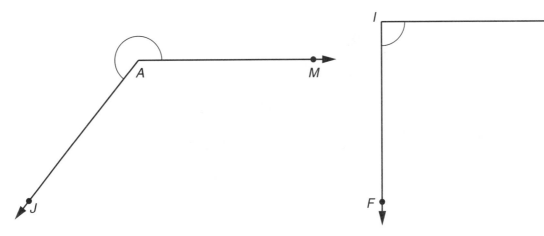

∠*JAM* measures about _____.   ∠*FIN* measures about _____.

23. Circle the reflex angle in Problem 22.

What is the name of the other angle? _____

Solve. Do not use a calculator.

24. $756 \div 9 =$ _____   **25.** $308 * 42 =$ _____   **26.** $312 \div 12 =$ _____

27. $5.63 * 28 =$ _____   **28.** $92.4 / 6 =$ _____   **29.** $4.6 * 24.8 =$ _____

30. $3\frac{1}{2} + 2\frac{1}{8} =$ _____   **31.** $2\frac{1}{8} - \frac{5}{3} =$ _____   **32.** $3\frac{5}{10} + \frac{3}{4} =$ _____

LESSON 12·9 **End-of-Year Assessment** *continued*

33. Mark the following points on the ruler.

A: $\frac{7}{8}$ B: $\frac{3}{4}$ C: $1\frac{5}{16}$ D: $2\frac{11}{16}$ E: $\frac{5}{10}$

34. Write the prime factorization for 186. _____

Write each fraction in its simplest form.

35. $\frac{28}{3}$ = _____

36. $4\frac{18}{24}$ = _____

37. $\frac{43}{6}$ = _____

38. $\frac{70}{5}$ = _____

39. $9\frac{36}{60}$ = _____

40. $11\frac{54}{72}$ = _____

41. If $\frac{4}{5}$ of a set is 12, how many are in the whole set? _____

Explain your solution strategy. _____

_____

Write >, <, or =.

42. -3 _____ 3

43. -15 _____ -10

44. -0.5 _____ -0.75

45. $-7 + 7$ _____ 0

46. $-4 - (-8)$ _____ $2 + (-5)$

47. $17 + (-3)$ _____ $10 + 10$

48. Circle the number sentences that are true.

$5 + (7 * 5) = 40$ $36 = 2^2 + 4 * 8$ $30 / (2 + 8) + 5 = 28$

$0 = (-5 + 3) * 2$ $40 - 15 / 5 + 2 = 39$ $18 / 3 + 3 * 4 = \frac{3}{4}$

End-of-Year Assessment *continued*

LESSON 12·9

49. Write an open number sentence. Then solve the problem.

Maureen was cleaning her collection of toy elephants. She had already cleaned 24 of them. If that was $\frac{6}{7}$ of them, how many did she have left to clean?

Open sentence: _____

Answer: _____

Explain: _____

_____

50. Complete the table. Then graph the data in the table.

Rule: Number of words = minutes * 46 words

Time (min)	Number of words
1	
4	184
3	
	92
	115

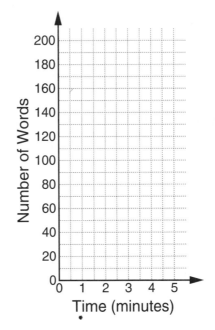

51. What is the volume of the prism to the right?

_____
(unit)

3 in.

4 in.   2 in.

Volume of a prism: $V = B * h$

52. A cylindrical can has a base with an area of 21.5 square centimeters. It has a height of 10 centimeters.

What is its volume? _____
(unit)

Volume of a cylinder: $V = B * h$

LESSON 12·9 | **End-of-Year Assessment** *continued*

Part B

Find the missing number.

53. $\dfrac{1}{5} = \dfrac{19}{x}$ $x =$ _____

54. $\dfrac{8}{20} = \dfrac{s}{10}$ $s =$ _____

55. $\dfrac{n}{120} = \dfrac{3}{4}$ $n =$ _____

56. $\dfrac{36}{m} = \dfrac{4}{7}$ $m =$ _____

Complete the table.

	Exponential Notation	Standard Notation	Number-and-Word Notation
57.	$2 * 10^3$		
58.		8,000,000	
59.			4.6 hundred-million
60.	$2.3 * 10^9$		

61. Pairs of cargo pants sell for $18.00 each. With a shopper's card, the price is discounted 25%. There is an additional 10% off the total cost if you buy two or more pairs. What is the discounted cost of 3 pairs of cargo pants? Show your work on the back of this page.

Discounted cost: _____

Find the greatest common factor for each pair of numbers below.

62. 24 and 60 _____

63. 100 and 25 _____

Find the least common multiple for each pair of numbers below.

64. 4 and 8 _____

65. 6 and 9 _____

LESSON 12·9 **End-of-Year Assessment** *continued*

66. Circle the figure below that has the greatest volume.

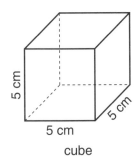

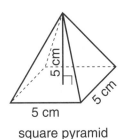

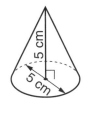

cube   square pyramid   cone

Volume of a prism: $V = B * h$

Volume of a pyramid: $V = \frac{1}{3} * (B * h)$

Volume of a cone: $V = \frac{1}{3} * (B * h)$

Explain. _____

_____

_____

_____

Solve. Write your answers in simplest form.

67. a. $\frac{7}{8} * \frac{14}{16} =$ _____ **b.** $12\frac{3}{5} * \frac{5}{6} =$ _____ **c.** $4\frac{2}{7} * 3\frac{1}{6} =$ _____

68. a. $\frac{3}{8} \div \frac{2}{16} =$ _____ **b.** $17\frac{3}{5} \div 2\frac{12}{25} =$ _____ **c.** $\frac{1}{2} \div \frac{5}{6} =$ _____

GRADE 6 Beginning-of-Year Assessment

1. Compare using $>$, $<$, or $=$.

   a. 7 hundredths _____ 0.07

   b. 6,300,000 _____ 6.1 million

   c. $6.2 * 10^{-2}$ _____ $7 * 10^{-3}$

   d. 2^4 _____ 24

   e. 0.80 _____ $\frac{35}{40}$

   f. 0.02 _____ 20%

2. Divide. Write your answers in simplest form.

   a. $\frac{1}{4} \div 4 =$ _____

   b. $3\frac{4}{7} \div \frac{1}{2} =$ _____

   c. $6\frac{1}{5} \div 2\frac{3}{8} =$ _____

3. Use order of operations to evaluate each expression.

   a. $12 \div 3 + 2 * 8 =$ _____

   b. $7 + 4 * 6 \div 2 - (-6) =$ _____

4. Estimate each quotient.

   a. $39.75 \div 0.5$ Estimate _____

   b. $50 \div 1.4$ Estimate _____

5. Complete the table for the given rule. Then plot the points and connect them to make a line graph.

   Rule: $y = 3x + 2$

x	y
−2	
	−1
0	
1	
	8

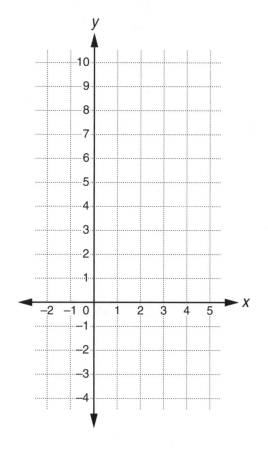

GRADE 6 | **Beginning-of-Year Assessment**

6. Solve.

a. $-36.7 + (-12.3) =$ _____

b. $-\frac{9}{10} + \frac{14}{15} =$ _____

c. _____ $= \frac{49}{-7}$

d. _____ $= -60 \div (-0.5)$

7. Is each number sentence true or false?

a. $-15 * (6 - 8) < 20$ _____

b. $10 * (3 \div (-3)) \geq -3 \div \frac{7}{8}$ _____

c. $(-2)^3 > (-2)^2$ _____

d. $(8 * 45) + 20 = 8 * (45 + 20)$ _____

Solve each equation. Show your work.

8. $2d + 8 = 24$

9. $2p + 3 + 4p = 15$

$d =$ _____

$p =$ _____

10. $\frac{4}{9}k + 9 = \frac{7}{9}k - 18$

11. $12r - 52 = 20 - 6r$

$k =$ _____

$r =$ _____

12. Graph the solution set for each inequality.

a. $m \geq 1 - 2$

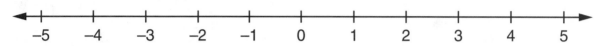

-5 -4 -3 -2 -1 0 1 2 3 4 5

b. $n < -2$

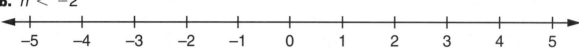

-5 -4 -3 -2 -1 0 1 2 3 4 5

13. Tyree flips a coin two times.

a. Make an organized list or a tree diagram to display all possible outcomes.

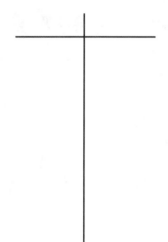

b. What is the probability Tyree will get 2 HEADS? Express this probability as a percent.

_____

14. Marki rolled a fair die 4 times and recorded the result of each roll in the table at the right.

roll	1st	2nd	3rd	4th
number rolled	3	2	1	2

a. What is the probability that the die will land on 2 when Marki rolls again? Express the probability as a fraction. _____

b. About how many times would you expect Marki to get a 3 if she rolls the same fair die 468 times? _____ times

Beginning-of-Year Assessment

Solve each problem using any method.

15. Model airplane hobbyists can collect airplanes and equipment that are precise replicas of actual planes. The toy planes look exactly like the real planes they represent, only smaller.

There are four popular scales that appear in the table at the right.

Scale Name	Scale (inches) Model: Actual
A	$\frac{1}{48}$
B	$\frac{1}{150}$
C	$\frac{1}{200}$
D	$\frac{1}{500}$

a. An Air National Guard F-16 is 48 ft long. What is the length in inches of a model F-16 plane built on the A scale?

_____ in.

b. A B-scale cargo transporter is 8 inches long. How long is the actual plane?

_____ ft

c. A commercial 727 passenger plane is $162\frac{1}{2}$ ft long. A model is 9.75 in. long. In which scale was the model built? _____ scale

16. A 10-oz can of *Math-O's* costs $3.29. A 14-oz can costs $4.34. Which can is the better buy?

a. The _____-oz can of *Math-O's* is the better buy.

b. Explain how you determined which can is the better buy.

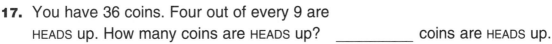

_____

_____

_____

_____

_____

17. You have 36 coins. Four out of every 9 are HEADS up. How many coins are HEADS up? _____ coins are HEADS up.

Beginning-of-Year Assessment

18. Triangles *MNO* and *PQR* are similar.

   a. Measure the sides of each triangle to the nearest millimeter. Write the measurements next to the sides.

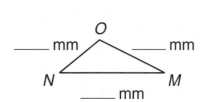

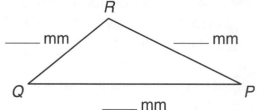

   b. What is the size-change ratio between the two triangles? _____

19. Lines *p* and *q* are parallel and intersect the *x*- and *y*-axes to form similar right triangles.

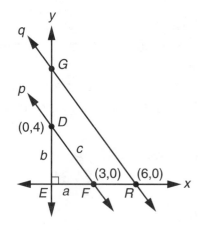

   a. What are the coordinates of point *G*?

      (_____, _____)

   b. Find the area of triangle *DEF*.

      Area = _____ units²

   c. Use the Pythagorean theorem to find the length of $\overline{DF}$.

Pythagorean theorem
$a^2 + b^2 = c^2$

      $\overline{DF}$ = _____ units

   d. Explain how you can use the dimensions of triangle *DEF* to find the perimeter of triangle *GER*.

_____

_____

_____

_____

Beginning-of-Year Assessment

20. Write each number as a percent.

a. 0.4 _____   **b.** 0.035 _____   **c.** 1.2 _____   **d.** 0.07 _____

21. Complete the table. Write each fraction in simplest form.

	Fraction	Decimal	Percent
a.	$\frac{4}{5}$		
b.			26%
c.		0.08	
d.		0.002	

Solve Problems 22–26 using any method. Show your work.

22. Find 48% of 50.

23. What percent of 50 is 41?

48% of 50 is _____.

41 is _____% of 50.

24. 80 is 20% of what number?

25. Find 130% of 60.

80 is 20% of _____.

130% of 60 is _____.

26. Software for a personal computer that regularly sells
for $80 is on sale for 15% off. Find the sale price.

Sale price _____

GRADE 6 | Beginning-of-Year Assessment *cont.*

For Problems 27–30, write an equation to solve for *x*.
Find any missing dimensions. You may use a calculator.

Formulas	
Areas	
Rectangle	$b * h$
Circle	πr^2
Volume	
Rectangular prism	$B * h$
Cylinder	$B * h$

27. Regular pentagon

Perimeter: 75 units

a. Equation _____ **b.** $x =$ _____ **c.** side = _____ units

28.

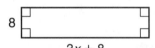

Area: 280 units²

a. Equation _____ **b.** $x =$ _____ **c.** base = _____ units

29.

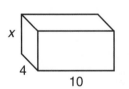

Volume: 200 units³

a. Equation _____

b. $x =$ _____ units

30.

Volume: 792 units³

Use $\pi = \frac{22}{7}$

a. Equation _____

b. $x =$ _____ units

Beginning-of-Year Assessment

31. Find the measure of each angle without using a protractor. Lines *m* and *n* are parallel.

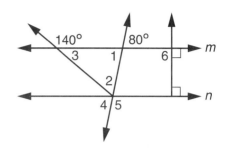

  a. m∠1 = _____

  b. m∠2 = _____

  c. m∠3 = _____

  d. m∠4 = _____

  e. m∠5 = _____

  f. m∠6 = _____

Use triangle *ABC* with vertices at (6, 0); (9, 4); and (3,4) to complete Problem 32.

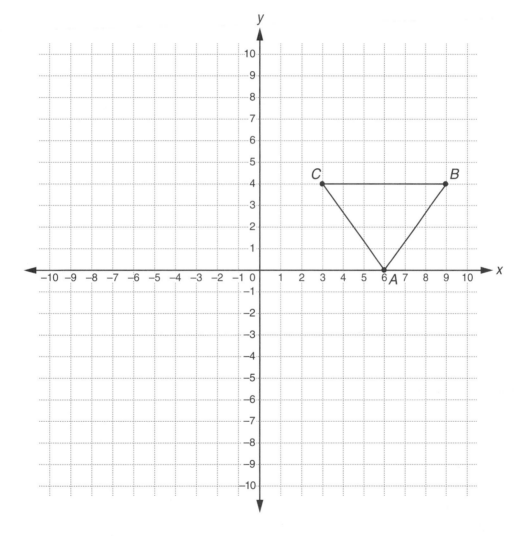

32. Draw and label the image of triangle *ABC* after

  a. a reflection over the *y*-axis.   *A*′(____,____); *B*′(____,____); *C*′(____,____)

  b. a translation 6 units down.   *A*″(____,____); *B*″(____,____); *C*″(____,____)

33. For each figure shown below, draw the line(s) of reflection symmetry. Then determine the order of rotation symmetry for the figure.

a.

b.

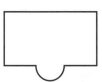

c.

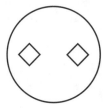

Order of
rotation symmetry _____

Order of
rotation symmetry _____

Order of
rotation symmetry _____

34. Write an equation you can use to find the value of *s* so the rectangle and the triangle have the same perimeter. Then find the perimeter. Show your work.

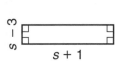

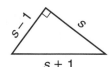

a. Equation _____

b. *s* = _____

c. Perimeter = _____ units

35. Solve each equation. Then check your solution. Show your work.

a. $3k = 2(2k - 3)$

b. $9(11 - m) = 19 + m$

$k =$ _____

$m =$ _____

Check: _____

Check: _____

LESSON 5·11 **Mid-Year Assessment**

Part A

1. The ages of the teachers at Composite Middle School are represented by the following data set:

   56, 32, 34, 29, 24, 43, 26, 39, 45, 37, 50, 34, 55, 62, 29, 34, 47, 52, 49

   a. Construct a stem-and-leaf plot to represent the age data.

Ages of Teachers at Composite Middle School	
Stems (10s)	Leaves (1s)

   b. Use your stem-and-leaf plot to find the following landmarks:

   Range _____

   Mode(s) _____

   Median _____

2. George's math test scores are 82, 59, 91, and 88.

   a. Find the median and the mean score.   Median _____   Mean _____

   b. Is the median or the mean the better representation of George's overall performance, or are they about the same? Explain your reasoning.

   _____

   _____

   _____

   c. Suppose George needs a mean score of 83 to earn a B in his math class and there is only one test left to take. What is the least score George can receive on this last test to get a B for the class?

   _____ Explain how you got your answer. _____

   _____

   _____

   _____

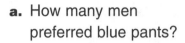

Mid-Year Assessment *continued*

3. A clothing designer surveyed adult women and men on the color of pants they preferred to wear for formal occasions. The stacked bar graph below displays the results of that survey.

a. How many men preferred blue pants?

_____

b. Which pant color did the majority of men prefer?

_____

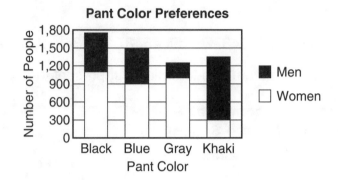

c. About what fraction of people who preferred gray pants were women?

About _____

4. The Mouawad Splendour diamond sold for 12.76 million dollars in 1990. Write 12.76 million in

a. standard notation. _____

b. scientific notation. _____

5. The moon orbits at an average distance from Earth of about 384,400 kilometers. Write 384,400 in

a. number-and-word notation. _____

b. expanded notation. (___ * 10⁻) + (___ * 10⁻) + (___ * 10⁻) + (___ * 10⁻)

6. An angstrom (Å) is a unit of length.
   It is equivalent to 0.0000001 millimeter.
   Write 0.0000001 as a power of 10. _____

LESSON
5·11

Mid-Year Assessment *continued*

Find each sum, difference, and quotient. Express any remainders as simplified fractions. Show your work.

7. $93.701 + 115.39 =$ _____   **8.** $96.8 - 15.92 =$ _____

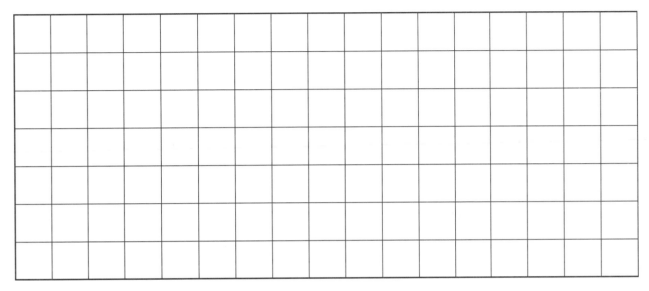

9. $762 \div 24 =$ _____   **10.** $328 \overline{)63,509} =$ _____

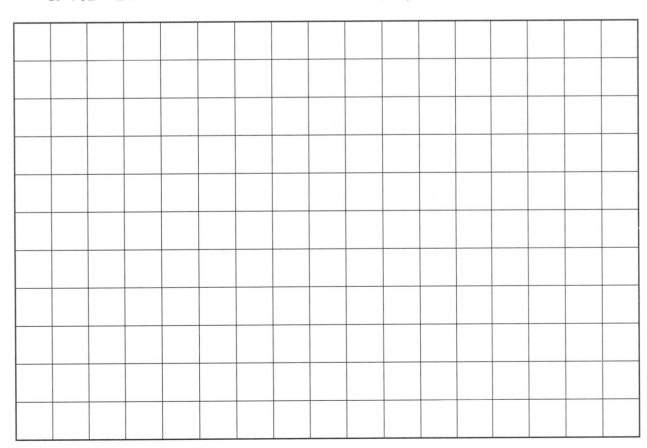

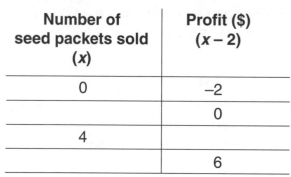

Mid-Year Assessment *continued*

The Science Club is selling packets of flower seeds. They spend $2 buying 40 packets of seeds at $0.05 each. They plan to charge $1 for each seed packet.

Number of seed packets sold (x)	Profit ($) (x – 2)
0	–2
	0
4	
	6

11. Complete the table at the right.

12. Use the grid at the right to graph the profit data from the table. Connect the points.

Use the graph you made in Problem 12 to answer the following questions.

13. How many packets of seeds must the club sell to make a profit of $5?

_____

14. What does the point $(0, -2)$ on the graph represent?

_____

_____

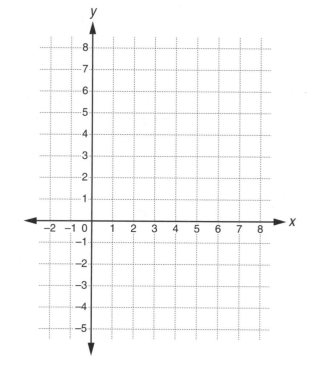

15. Order from least to greatest.

a. $\frac{5}{8}, \frac{3}{8}, \frac{1}{5}, \frac{3}{5}, \frac{1}{8}$ _____

b. $2.1, \frac{22}{10}, 2.01, \frac{5}{2}, \frac{22}{11}$ _____

16. Solve. Write each answer in simplest form.

a. $7 - 4\frac{3}{4} =$ _____

b. $\frac{4}{9} + \frac{5}{6} =$ _____

c. $3\frac{4}{5} - 2\frac{2}{3} =$ _____

d. $3\frac{3}{4} * 4\frac{2}{5} =$ _____

LESSON 5·11 Mid-Year Assessment *continued*

17. Complete the table. Simplify all fractions.

	Fraction	Decimal	Percent		Fraction	Decimal	Percent
a.		0.55		e.			35%
b.			$12\frac{1}{2}\%$	f.	$\frac{3}{8}$		
c.	$\frac{13}{52}$			g.		0.78	
d.		0.045		h.	$\frac{4}{5}$		

Ms. McCarty's math students asked a total of 200 adults what time they left for work each weekday morning. The results of their survey appear in the table below.

18. Complete the table. Round measures to the nearest whole degree.

Departure Times for Work	Number of People	Percent of Total	Degree Measure of Sector
Before 6 A.M.	80	a.	b.
Between 6 A.M. and 7 A.M.	54	c.	d.
Between 7 A.M. and 8 A.M.	40	e.	72°
After 8 A.M.	f.	13%	g.
Total	200	100%	360°

19. Use a protractor to make a circle graph that displays the information above. Do not use the Percent Circle. Write a title for the graph.

20. Based on the survey results in Problem 18, about how many of 250 people would you expect to say that they left for work between 6 A.M. and 7 A.M.?

_____ people

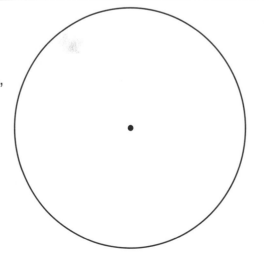

LESSON 5·11 **Mid-Year Assessment** *continued*

21. Write an algebraic expression, using the suggested variable, to answer each of the following questions.

  a. A tarantula spider has 8 legs. How many legs do *t* tarantulas have? _____ legs

  b. Christina has *d* dollars. Her brother has $8 more than she has. How much money does Christina's brother have? _____ dollars

  c. Bobbie's dog is *y* years old. How old was Bobbie's dog 8 years ago? _____ years old

22. Evaluate each expression when $x = 3$.

  a. $9.2 * 10^x$ _____

  b. $2^x * x$ _____

  c. $10^{-x} * 5^x$ _____

  d. $x^0 - 8$ _____

23. Quadrilateral *PALE* is a parallelogram. Without using a protractor, find the degree measure of

  a. $\angle ALE$. _____ °

  b. $\angle AEL$. _____ °

  c. $\angle PEL$. _____ °

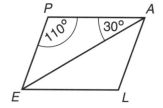

24. Without using a protractor, find the degree measure of each numbered angle.

  a. $m\angle 1 =$ _____ °

  b. $m\angle 2 =$ _____ °

  c. $m\angle 3 =$ _____ °

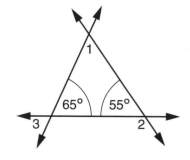

LESSON 5·11

Mid-Year Assessment *continued*

Part B

25. Graph the quadrilateral with the vertices given below. Label each vertex with the appropriate letter. Vertex *Y* has been plotted and labeled for you.

Y (1,2) E (3,4)

A (6,0) R (4,–2)

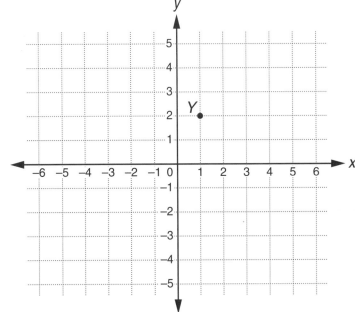

26. Without graphing the image, list the vertices of *Y'E'A'R'* resulting from translating each vertex of *YEAR* 1 unit left and 2 units up.

Y'(____, ____); E'(____, ____); A'(____, ____); R'(____, ____)

27. Reflect *YEAR* (Problem 25) over the *y*-axis. Label the reflected image *Y"E"A"R"*.

28. This past summer, Vivian and her sister started a lawn-mowing and landscaping business. For four months, they recorded their income and expenses in the spreadsheet below. Use the spreadsheet to answer the questions that follow.

	A	B	C	D	E	F
1		May	June	July	August	Total
2	Income	$20.00	$65.50	$75.00	$55.75	
3	Expenses	$30.70	$5.15	$0.00	$5.85	

a. During which month did Vivian and her sister have the most expenses? _____

b. In which cell does the business's July income appear? _____

c. Complete Column F of the spreadsheet above.

d. Write a spreadsheet formula you could use to find the mean income for the 4 months.

_____

LESSON 5·11 | **Mid-Year Assessment** *continued*

29. Find the missing numbers.

a. $\frac{6}{16} = \frac{x}{48}$ $x =$ _____

b. $\frac{20}{30} = \frac{w}{12}$ $w =$ _____

30. Use your ruler or Geometry Template to draw a rectangle with a base of $2\frac{3}{8}$ inches and a height of $\frac{13}{16}$ inch. Label the base and the height.

31. What is the perimeter of the rectangle? _____ in.

32. What is the area of the rectangle? _____ in²

33. Solve.

a. $\frac{1}{10}$ of a number is 5. What is the number? _____

b. $\frac{2}{3}$ of 27 = _____   c. 5% of 120 = _____

d. 20% of a number is 8. What is the number? _____

34. Estimate each quotient.

a. $146 \div 6$ _____   b. $557.8 \div 48$ _____

c. $259 \div 4.8$ _____   d. $11.89 \div 2.9$ _____

35. Suppose you want to share $175.68 equally among 32 people. How much money should each person get? Show your work.

$_____

LESSON 10·6 | **End-of-Year Assessment**

Part A

1. Compare using $>$, $<$, or $=$.

a. 7 hundredths _____ 0.007

b. 5,400,000 _____ 5.2 million

c. $3.4 * 10^{-2}$ _____ $5 * 10^{-3}$

d. 3^3 _____ 33

e. 0.95 _____ $\frac{39}{40}$

f. 0.07 _____ 70%

2. Divide. Write your answers in simplest form.

a. $\frac{1}{3} \div 3 =$ _____

b. $2\frac{3}{5} \div \frac{1}{4} =$ _____

c. $7\frac{1}{8} \div 2\frac{2}{9} =$ _____

3. Use order of operations to evaluate each expression.

a. $3 * 5 + 16 \div 4 =$ _____

b. $5 + 3 * 9 \div 3 - (-7) =$ _____

4. Estimate each quotient.

a. $36.25 \div 0.5$ Estimate _____

b. $60 \div 1.2$ Estimate _____

5. Complete the table for the given rule. Then plot the points and connect them to make a line graph.

Rule: $y = 2x + 3$

x	y
−2	
	1
0	
1	
	7

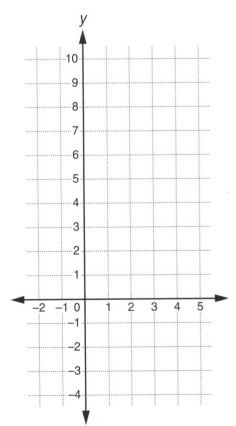

LESSON 10·6 | **End-of-Year Assessment** *continued*

6. Solve.

    a. $-45.9 + (-14.5) =$ _____

    b. $-\frac{7}{8} + \frac{11}{12} =$ _____

    c. _____ $= \frac{81}{-9}$

    d. _____ $= -70 \div (-0.5)$

7. Is each number sentence true or false?

    a. $(9 * 60) + 20 = 9 * (60 + 20)$ _____

    b. $-12 * (10 - 20) < 100$ _____

    c. $(-4)^3 > (-4)^2$ _____

    d. $16 * (8 \div (-8)) \leq -8 \div \frac{3}{4}$ _____

Solve each equation. Show your work.

8. $3c + 12 = 36$

9. $5y + 2 + 3y = 18$

    $c =$ _____

    $y =$ _____

10. $\frac{3}{8}x + 16 = \frac{9}{8}x - 20$

11. $18n - 20 = 36 - 10n$

    $x =$ _____

    $n =$ _____

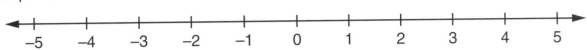

End-of-Year Assessment *continued*

12. Graph the solution set for each inequality.

a. $p \leq 3 - 4$

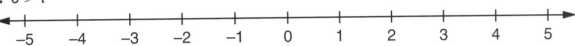

b. $0 > t$

13. Corbin flips a coin three times.

a. Make an organized list or a tree diagram to display all possible outcomes.

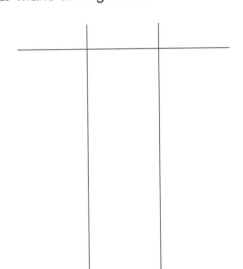

b. What is the probability Corbin will get 3 HEADS? Express
this probability as a percent.   _____

14. Marni rolled a fair die 5 times
and recorded the result of each
roll in the table at the right.

roll	1st	2nd	3rd	4th	5th
number rolled	6	5	6	2	6

a. What is the probability that the die will land on 6 when
Marni rolls again? Express the probability as a fraction. _____

b. About how many times would you expect Marni to
get a 3 if she rolls the same fair die 648 times? _____ times

LESSON 10·6 | **End-of-Year Assessment** *continued*

Solve each problem using any method.

15. Model railroad hobbyists can collect toy trains and equipment that are precise replicas of actual trains. The toy trains look exactly like the real trains they represent, only smaller.

There are four popular scales that appear in the table at the right.

Scale Name	Scale (inches) Model: Actual
N	$\frac{1}{160}$
HO	$\frac{1}{87}$
S	$\frac{1}{64}$
O	$\frac{1}{48}$

a. Each car on a full-size passenger train is 80 ft long. What is the length in inches of a model passenger car built on the S scale?

_____ in.

b. An O-scale locomotive is 1.05 ft long. How long is the actual locomotive?

_____ ft

c. A boxcar on an actual freight train is 40 ft long. A model boxcar is 3 in. long. In which scale was the model built?

_____ scale

16. A 16-oz box of *Sweety Pi* breakfast cereal costs $3.68. A 20-oz box costs $4.79. Which box is the better buy?

a. The _____-oz box of cereal is the better buy.

b. Explain how you determined which box is the better buy.

_____

_____

_____

_____

17. You have 45 coins. Five out of every 9 are HEADS up. How many coins are HEADS up? _____ coins are HEADS up

LESSON 10·6 **End-of-Year Assessment** *continued*

18. Triangles *MAY* and *JUL* are similar.

a. Measure the sides of each triangle to the nearest millimeter. Write the measurements next to the sides.

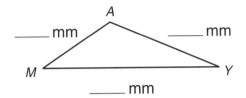
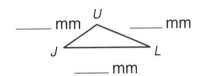

b. What is the size-change ratio between the two triangles? _____

19. Lines *p* and *q* are parallel and intersect the *x*- and *y*-axes to form similar right triangles.

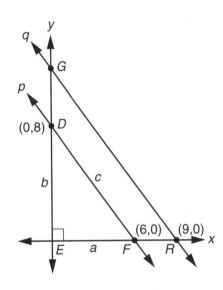

a. What are the coordinates of point *G*?

(_____, _____)

b. Find the area of triangle *DEF*.

Area = _____ units^2

c. Use the Pythagorean theorem to find the length of $\overline{DF}$.

$\overline{DF}$ = _____ units

Pythagorean theorem
$a^2 + b^2 = c^2$

d. Explain how you can use the dimensions of triangle *DEF* to find the perimeter of triangle *GER*.

_____

_____

_____

_____

LESSON 10·6 | **End-of-Year Assessment** *continued*

20. Write each number as a percent.

   a. 0.3 _____   **b.** 0.021 _____   **c.** 1.5 _____   **d.** 0.09 _____

21. Complete the table. Write each fraction in simplest form.

	Fraction	Decimal	Percent
a.	$\frac{7}{8}$		
b.			72%
c.		0.06	
d.		0.005	

Solve Problems 22–26 using any method. Show your work.

22. Find 56% of 75.

   56% of 75 is _____.

23. What percent of 25 is 17?

   17 is _____% of 25.

24. 120 is 15% of what number?

   120 is 15% of _____.

25. Find 150% of 90.

   150% of 90 is _____.

26. Software for a personal digital assistant (PDA) that regularly sells for $60 is on sale for 15% off. Find the sale price.

   Sale price _____

End-of-Year Assessment *continued*

For Problems 27–30, write an equation to solve for *x*.
Find any missing dimensions. You may use a calculator.

Formulas
Areas
Rectangle $b * h$
Circle πr^2
Volume
Rectangular prism $B * h$
Cylinder $B * h$

27. Regular pentagon

     Perimeter: 90 units

a. Equation _____

b. $x =$ _____

c. side = _____ units

28. 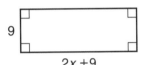   Area: 225 units^2

a. Equation _____

b. $x =$ _____

c. base = _____ units

29.

Volume: 396 units^3

a. Equation _____

b. $x =$ _____ units

30.

Volume: 1,078 units^3

Use $\pi = \frac{22}{7}$

a. Equation _____

b. $x =$ _____ units

LESSON 10·6 | **End-of-Year Assessment** *continued*

31. Find the measure of each angle without using a protractor. Lines *m* and *n* are parallel.

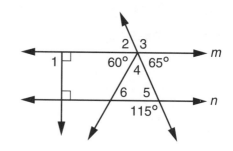

    a. m∠1 = _____

    b. m∠2 = _____

    c. m∠3 = _____

    d. m∠4 = _____

    e. m∠5 = _____

    f. m∠6 = _____

Use triangle *ABC* with vertices at (5,4), (7,8), and (3,8) to complete Problem 32.

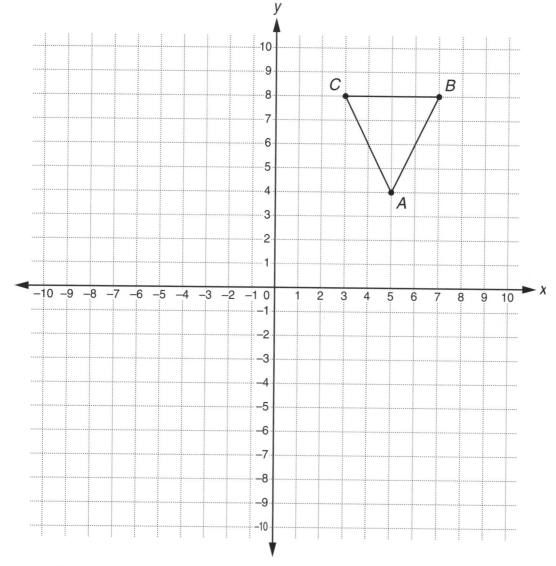

32. Draw and label the image of triangle *ABC* after

    a. a reflection over the *y*-axis.   *A'*(___,___); *B'*(___,___); *C'*(___,___)

    b. a translation 6 units down.   *A''*(___,___); *B''*(___,___); *C''*(___,___)

LESSON 10·6 | **End-of-Year Assessment** *continued*

Part B

33. For each figure shown below, draw the line(s) of reflection symmetry. Then determine the order of rotation symmetry for the figure.

a.

Order of rotation symmetry _____

b.

Order of rotation symmetry _____

c.

Order of rotation symmetry _____

34. Write an equation you can use to find the value of s so the rectangle and the triangle have the same perimeter. Then find the perimeter. Show your work.

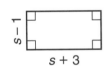   

a. Equation _____

b. $s =$ _____

c. Perimeter = _____ units

35. Solve each equation. Then check your solution. Show your work.

a. $7k = 3(5k - 8)$

b. $6(m - 3) = 4(m + 3)$

$k =$ _____

$m =$ _____

Check: _____

Check: _____

Individual Profile of Progress

Name _____ Date _____

Tasks	Content Assessed	Child's Responses	Comments
1	**Count on by 1s.** [Number and Numeration Goal 1]	Counts on to _____.	
2	**Count back by 1s.** [Number and Numeration Goal 1]	Counts back from _____.	
3	**Count objects.** [Number and Numeration Goal 2]	Counts _____ objects.	
4	**Read numbers.** [Number and Numeration Goal 3]	Numbers read: _____ _____ _____	
5	**Compare and order numbers.** [Number and Numeration Goal 6]	Range of numbers compared: _____	
6	**Compare sizes of objects.** [Measurement and Reference Frames Goal 1]	Size comparison language used: _____ _____ _____	
7	**Recognize 2-dimensional geometric shapes.** [Geometry Goal 1]	Recognizes: Circle _____ Triangle _____ Square _____ Rectangle _____	
8	**Identify shapes having line symmetry.** [Geometry Goal 2]	Objects used: _____ Recognizes matching sides? _____	
9	**Extend a pattern.** [Patterns, Functions, and Algebra Goal 1]	Pattern used: _____ Extends? _____	
10	**Use a rule to sort objects.** [Patterns, Functions, and Algebra Goal 1]	Sorts by rule? _____ Rule used: _____	

Class Checklist

Class _____

Date _____

Names	1. Count on by 1s to ___. [Number and Numeration Goal 1]	2. Count back by 1s from ___. [Number and Numeration Goal 1]	3. Count ___ objects. [Number and Numeration Goal 2]	4. Read numbers. [Number and Numeration Goal 3]	5. Compare and order numbers. [Number and Numeration Goal 6]	6. Compare sizes of objects. [Measurement and Reference Frames Goal 1]	7. Recognize 2-dimensional geometric shapes. [Geometry Goal 1]	8. Identify shapes having line symmetry. [Geometry Goal 2]	9. Extend a pattern. [Patterns, Functions, and Algebra Goal 1]	10. Use a rule to sort objects. [Patterns, Functions, and Algebra Goal 1]
1.										
2.										
3.										
4.										
5.										
6.										
7.										
8.										
9.										
10.										
11.										
12.										
13.										
14.										
15.										
16.										
17.										
18.										
19.										
20.										
21.										
22.										
23.										
24.										
25.										

Individual Profile of Progress

_____

Name   Date

Task	Content Assessed	Child's Responses	Assess Progress	Comments
1	**Count on by 1s.** [Number and Numeration Goal 1]	Counts on to _____.		
2	**Count back by 1s.** [Number and Numeration Goal 1]	Counts back from _____.		
3a	**Count on by 5s.** [Number and Numeration Goal 1]	Counts on to _____.		
3b	**Count on by 10s.** [Number and Numeration Goal 1]	Counts on to _____.		
4	**Count objects.** [Number and Numeration Goal 2]	Counts _____ objects.		
5	**Estimate the number of objects in a collection.** [Number and Numeration Goal 2]	Understands concept of estimation? _____		
6	**Model numbers with manipulatives.** [Number and Numeration Goal 3]	Numbers modeled: _____ _____ _____		
7	**Read and write (or dictate) 2-digit numbers.** [Number and Numeration Goal 3]	Range of numbers read and written (or dictated): _____ _____ _____		
8	**Compare and order numbers.** [Number and Numeration Goal 6]	Range of numbers compared: _____ _____ _____		
9a	**Solve number stories.** [Operations and Computation Goal 1]	Problem solved: _____ _____ _____ Strategies: _____ _____		

Assess Progress: **A** = adequate progress   **N** = not adequate progress   **N/A** = not assessed

Name _____ Date _____

Task	Content Assessed	Child's Responses	Assess Progress	Comments
9b	**Identify join and take-away situations.** [Operations and Computation Goal 2]	Identifies: Join _____ Take-away _____		
10	**Describe events using basic probability terms.** [Data and Chance Goal 3]	Terms used: _____ _____ _____		
11	**Use nonstandard tools and techniques to estimate and compare weight and length.** [Measurement and Reference Frames Goal 1]	Compare length? _____ Compare weight? _____ Tools used: _____ _____		
12	**Identify 2-dimensional geometric shapes.** [Geometry Goal 1]	Identifies: Circle _____ Triangle _____ Square _____ Rectangle _____		
13	**Identify shapes having line symmetry.** [Geometry Goal 2]	Objects used: _____ Recognizes line symmetry? _____		
14	**Extend, describe, and create patterns.** [Patterns, Functions, and Algebra Goal 1]	Extends: _____ Describes: _____ Creates (show pattern): _____		
15	**Use a rule to sort objects.** [Patterns, Functions, and Algebra Goal 1]	Sorts by specified rule? _____ Rule used: _____ Sorts by self-chosen rule? _____ Rule used: _____		

Assess Progress: **A** = adequate progress   **N** = not adequate progress   **N/A** = not assessed

Class Checklist

Class _____

Date _____

Names	1. Count on by 1s to ___. [Number and Numeration Goal 1]	2. Count back by 1s from ___. [Number and Numeration Goal 1]	3a. Count on by 5s to ___. [Number and Numeration Goal 1]	3b. Count on by 10s to ___. [Number and Numeration Goal 1]	4. Count ___ objects. [Number and Numeration Goal 2]	5. Estimate the number of objects in a collection. [Number and Numeration Goal 2]	6. Model numbers with manipulatives. [Number and Numeration Goal 3]	7. Read and write (or dictate) 2-digit numbers to ___. [Number and Numeration Goal 3]
1.								
2.								
3.								
4.								
5.								
6.								
7.								
8.								
9.								
10.								
11.								
12.								
13.								
14.								
15.								
16.								
17.								
18.								
19.								
20.								
21.								
22.								
23.								
24.								
25.								

Assess Progress: **A** = adequate progress **N** = not adequate progress   **N/A** = not assessed

Class Checklist *cont.*

Class _____

Date _____

Names	8. Compare and order numbers to _____. [Number and Numeration Goal 6]	9a. Solve number stories. [Operations and Computation Goal 1]	9b. Identify join and take-away situations. [Operations and Computation Goal 1]	10. Describe events using basic probability terms. [Data and Chance Goal 3]	11. Use nonstandard tools and techniques to estimate and compare weight and length. [Measurement and Reference Frames Goal 1]	12. Identify 2-dimensional geometric shapes. [Geometry Goal 1]	13. Identify shapes having line symmetry. [Geometry Goal 2]	14. Extend, describe, and create patterns. [Patterns, Functions, and Algebra Goal 1]	15. Use a rule to sort objects. [Patterns, Functions, and Algebra Goal 1]
1.									
2.									
3.									
4.									
5.									
6.									
7.									
8.									
9.									
10.									
11.									
12.									
13.									
14.									
15.									
16.									
17.									
18.									
19.									
20.									
21.									
22.									
23.									
24.									
25.									

Assess Progress: **A** = adequate progress   **N** = not adequate progress   **N/A** = not assessed

Individual Profile of Progress

Name _____   Date _____

Tasks	Content Assessed	Child's Responses	Assess Progress	Comments
1	**Count on by 1s.** [Number and Numeration Goal 1]	Counts on to _____.		
2	**Count back by 1s.** [Number and Numeration Goal 1]	Counts back from _____.		
3a	**Count on by 2s.** [Number and Numeration Goal 1]	Counts on to _____.		
3b	**Count on by 5s.** [Number and Numeration Goal 1]	Counts on to _____.		
3c	**Count on by 10s.** [Number and Numeration Goal 1]	Counts on to _____.		
4	**Count objects.** [Number and Numeration Goal 2]	Counts _____ objects.		
5	**Estimate the number of objects in a collection.** [Number and Numeration Goal 2]	Understands concept of estimation? _____		
6	**Model numbers with manipulatives.** [Number and Numeration Goal 3]	Numbers modeled: _____ _____ _____		
7	**Exchange 1s for 10s and 10s for 100.** [Number and Numeration Goal 3]	Understands 1s for 10 exchange? _____ Understands 10s for 100 exchange? _____		
8	**Read and write (or dictate) 2-digit numbers.** [Number and Numeration Goal 3]	Range of numbers read and written (or dictated): _____ _____ _____		
9	**Use manipulatives to model half of a region or collection.** [Number and Numeration Goal 4]	Understands half? _____		

Assess Progress: **A** = adequate progress   **N** = not adequate progress   **N/A** = not assessed

Individual Profile of Progress *cont.*

Name _____   Date _____

Task	Content Assessed	Child's Responses	Assess Progress	Comments
10	**Give equivalent names for numbers.** [Number and Numeration Goal 5]	Number given: _____ Some equivalent names given: _____ _____ _____		
11	**Compare and order numbers.** [Number and Numeration Goal 6]	Range of numbers compared: _____		
12a	**Solve number stories.** [Operations and Computation Goal 1]	Problem solved: _____ _____ _____ Strategies: _____ _____		
12b	**Identify join and take-away situations.** [Operations and Computation Goal 2]	Identifies: Join _____ Take-away _____		
12c	**Read and write expressions and number sentences using the symbols $+$, $-$, and $=$.** [Patterns, Functions, and Algebra Goal 2]	Uses symbols correctly: $+$ _____ $-$ _____ $=$ _____		
13	**Use graphs to answer simple questions.** [Data and Chance Goal 2]	Questions answered: _____ _____		
14	**Describe events using basic probability terms.** [Data and Chance Goal 3]	Terms used: _____ _____ _____		

Assess Progress:  **A** = adequate progress   **N** = not adequate progress   **N/A** = not assessed

Name _____   Date _____

Task	Content Assessed	Child's Responses	Assess Progress	Comments
15	**Use nonstandard tools and techniques to estimate and compare weight and length.** [Measurement and Reference Frames Goal 1]	Compare length? _____ Compare weight? _____ Tools used: _____ _____		
16	**Identify pennies, nickels, dimes, quarters, and dollar bills.** [Measurement and Reference Frames Goal 2]	Penny _____ Nickel _____ Dime _____ Quarter _____ Dollar bill _____		
17	**Identify standard measuring tools.** [Measurement and Reference Frames Goals 1, 3, and 4]	Tools Identified: Ruler _____ Pan balance _____ Clock _____ Thermometer _____		
18	**Describe and use time periods relative to a day and week.** [Measurement and Reference Frames Goal 4]	Terms used: _____ _____ _____		
19a	**Identify 2-dimensional geometric shapes.** [Geometry Goal 1]	Identifies: Circle _____ Triangle _____ Square _____ Rectangle _____		
19b	**Identify 3-dimensional geometric solids.** [Geometry Goal 1]	Identifies: Cube _____ Sphere _____		

Assess Progress: **A** = adequate progress   **N** = not adequate progress   **N/A** = not assessed

Individual Profile of Progress *cont.*

Name _____   Date _____

Task	Content Assessed	Child's Responses	Assess Progress	Comments
20	**Identify shapes having line symmetry.** [Geometry Goal 2]	Objects used: _____ Recognizes line symmetry? _____		
21	**Extend, describe, and create patterns.** [Patterns, Functions, and Algebra Goal 1]	Extends: _____ Describes: _____ Creates (show pattern): _____		
22	**Use a rule to sort objects.** [Patterns, Functions, and Algebra Goal 1]	Sorts by different rules? _____		
23	**Use rules for *"What's My Rule?" Fishing* and other activities.** [Patterns, Functions, and Algebra Goal 1]	Understands "What's My Rule?" activities? _____		

Assess Progress: **A** = adequate progress   **N** = not adequate progress   **N/A** = not assessed

Notes

_____

_____

_____

_____

_____

_____

_____

_____

_____

_____

_____

Class _____

Date _____

Names	1. Count on by 1s to ___. [Number and Numeration Goal 1]	2. Count back by 1s from ___. [Number and Numeration Goal 1]	3a. Count on by 2s. [Number and Numeration Goal 1]	3b. Count on by 5s. [Number and Numeration Goal 1]	3c. Count on by 10s. [Number and Numeration Goal 1]	4. Count objects. [Number and Numeration Goal 1]	5. Estimate the number of objects in a collection. [Number and Numeration Goal 2]	6. Model numbers with manipulatives. [Number and Numeration Goal 3]	7. Exchange 1s for 10s and 10s for 100. [Number and Numeration Goal 3]	8. Read and write (or dictate) 2-digit numbers to ___. [Number and Numeration Goal 3]	9. Use manipulatives to model half of a region or collection. [Number and Numeration Goal 3]	10. Give equivalent names for numbers. [Number and Numeration Goal 4]	11. Compare and order numbers. [Number and Numeration Goal 5]	12a. Solve number stories. [Operations and Computation Goal 6]	12b. Identify join and take-away situations. [Operations and Computation Goal 1]
1.															
2.															
3.															
4.															
5.															
6.															
7.															
8.															
9.															
10.															
11.															
12.															
13.															
14.															
15.															
16.															
17.															
18.															
19.															
20.															
21.															
22.															
23.															
24.															
25.															

Assess Progress: **A** = adequate progress   **N** = not adequate progress   **N/A** = not assessed

Class _____

Date _____

Names	12c. Read and write expressions and number sentences using the symbols +, −, and =. [Patterns, Functions, and Algebra Goal 2]	13. Use graphs to answer simple questions. [Data and Chance Goal 2]	14. Describe events using basic probability terms. [Data and Chance Goal 3]	15. Use nonstandard tools and techniques to estimate and compare weight and length. [Measurement and Reference Frames Goal 1]	16. Identify pennies, nickels, dimes, quarters, and dollar bills. [Measurement and Reference Frames Goal 2]	17. Identify standard measuring tools. [Measurement and Reference Frames Goals 1, 3, and 4]	18. Describe and use time periods relative to a day and week. [Measurement and Reference Frames Goal 4]	19a. Identify 2-dimensional geometric shapes. [Geometry Goal 1]	19b. Identify 3-dimensional geometric solids. [Geometry Goal 1]	20. Identify shapes having line symmetry. [Geometry Goal 2]	21. Extend, describe, and create patterns. [Patterns, Functions, and Algebra Goal 1]	22. Use a rule to sort objects. [Patterns, Functions, and Algebra Goal 1]	23. Use rules for "What's My Rule" Fishing. [Patterns, Functions, and Algebra Goal 1]
1.													
2.													
3.													
4.													
5.													
6.													
7.													
8.													
9.													
10.													
11.													
12.													
13.													
14.													
15.													
16.													
17.													
18.													
19.													
20.													
21.													
22.													
23.													
24.													
25.													

Assess Progress: **A** = adequate progress   **N** = not adequate progress   **N/A** = not assessed

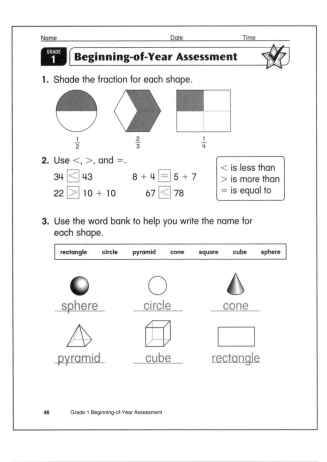

Name _____ **Date** _____ **Time** _____

GRADE 1 **Beginning-of-Year Assessment**

1. Shade the fraction for each shape.

$\frac{1}{2}$ $\frac{2}{3}$ $\frac{1}{4}$

2. Use <, >, and =.

| < is less than |
| > is more than |
| = is equal to |

34 $\boxed{<}$ 43   8 + 4 $\boxed{=}$ 5 + 7

22 $\boxed{>}$ 10 + 10   67 $\boxed{<}$ 78

3. Use the word bank to help you write the name for each shape.

| rectangle | circle | pyramid | cone | square | cube | sphere |

<u>sphere</u>   <u>circle</u>   <u>cone</u>

<u>pyramid</u>   <u>cube</u>   <u>rectangle</u>

46   Grade 1 Beginning-of-Year Assessment

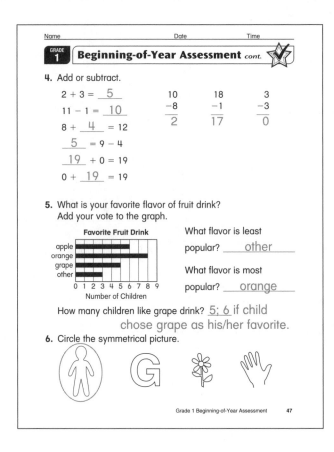

Name _____ **Date** _____ **Time** _____

GRADE 1 **Beginning-of-Year Assessment** *cont.*

4. Add or subtract.

2 + 3 = <u>5</u>

11 − 1 = <u>10</u>

8 + <u>4</u> = 12

<u>5</u> = 9 − 4

<u>19</u> + 0 = 19

0 + <u>19</u> = 19

10	18	3
−8	−1	−3
2	17	0

5. What is your favorite flavor of fruit drink? Add your vote to the graph.

Favorite Fruit Drink

apple
orange
grape
other

0 1 2 3 4 5 6 7 8 9
Number of Children

What flavor is least popular? <u>other</u>

What flavor is most popular? <u>orange</u>

How many children like grape drink? <u>5; 6</u> if child chose grape as his/her favorite.

6. Circle the symmetrical picture.

Grade 1 Beginning-of-Year Assessment   47

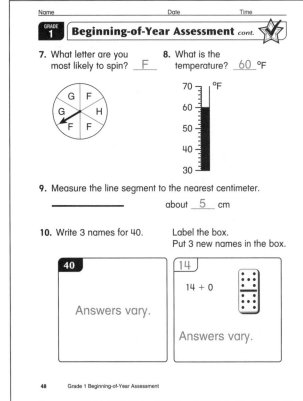

Name _____ **Date** _____ **Time** _____

GRADE 1 **Beginning-of-Year Assessment** *cont.*

7. What letter are you most likely to spin? <u>F</u>

G F
G H
F F

8. What is the temperature? <u>60</u> °F

9. Measure the line segment to the nearest centimeter.

about <u>5</u> cm

10. Write 3 names for 40.

40

Answers vary.

Label the box.
Put 3 new names in the box.

14

14 + 0

Answers vary.

48   Grade 1 Beginning-of-Year Assessment

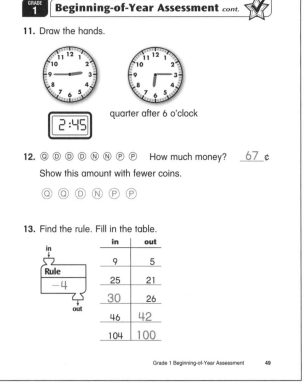

Name _____ **Date** _____ **Time** _____

GRADE 1 **Beginning-of-Year Assessment** *cont.*

11. Draw the hands.

quarter after 6 o'clock

2:45

12. Ⓠ Ⓠ Ⓓ Ⓓ Ⓝ Ⓝ Ⓟ Ⓟ   How much money? <u>67</u> ¢

Show this amount with fewer coins.

Ⓠ Ⓠ Ⓓ Ⓝ Ⓟ Ⓟ

13. Find the rule. Fill in the table.

in ↓

Rule
−4

out ↓

in	out
9	5
25	21
30	26
46	42
104	100

Grade 1 Beginning-of-Year Assessment   49

---

180   Grade 1 Assessment Answers

GRADE 1  **Beginning-of-Year Assessment** *cont.*

14. Write the numbers shown by the base-10 blocks.

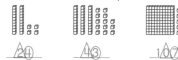

    24   43   107

Draw a ◯ around the ones place. Draw a △ around the tens place.

15. Sara has $1 Q Q D D N P P P $1. **78**

Luis has $1 D D D N N P P P $1. **43**

Who has more money? __Sara__

How much more money? __35¢ or $0.35__

16. Two people share these marbles equally.

How many marbles does each person get?

__7__ marbles

17. Solve. You may use your number grid.

46	59	28
−13	+30	−13
33	89	15

GRADE 1  **Beginning-of-Year Assessment** *cont.*

18. Add.

$3 + 4 =$ __7__ $10 + 6 =$ __16__

$30 + 40 =$ __70__ $20 + 6 =$ __26__

$300 + 400 =$ __700__ $30 + 6 =$ __36__

19. Solve.
Jack found 19 rocks at the lake.
Rosa found 30 rocks at the lake.
How many rocks did Jack and Rosa find in all?

__49__ rocks

Write a number model. __$19 + 30 = 49$__

20. What time is it?

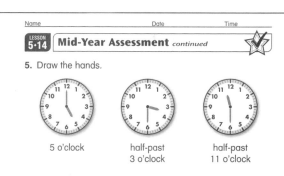

__10:20__   __9:05__

LESSON 5·14 **Mid-Year Assessment**

Part A

1.

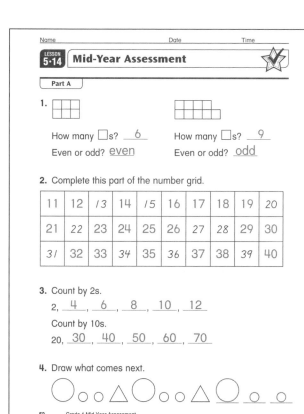

How many ☐s? __6__   How many ☐s? __9__

Even or odd? __even__   Even or odd? __odd__

2. Complete this part of the number grid.

11	12	13	14	15	16	17	18	19	20
21	22	23	24	25	26	27	28	29	30
31	32	33	34	35	36	37	38	39	40

3. Count by 2s.

2, __4__, __6__, __8__, __10__, __12__

Count by 10s.

20, __30__, __40__, __50__, __60__, __70__

4. Draw what comes next.

◯ ₒ ₒ △ ◯ ₒ ₒ △ ◯ ₒ ₒ

LESSON 5·14 **Mid-Year Assessment** *continued*

5. Draw the hands.

5 o'clock   half-past 3 o'clock   half-past 11 o'clock

6. Measure the line segment to the nearest inch.

about __2__ inches

7. Complete the tally chart.

Weather	Tallies	Total Days
Sunny	~~HHH~~ ~~HHH~~ ///	13
Cloudy	~~HHH~~ ~~HHH~~ ~~HHH~~	15
Rainy	~~HHH~~ ~~HHH~~ /	11
Snowy	~~HHH~~ ///	8

How many sunny days? __13__

How many more rainy days than snowy days?

__3__

Grade 1 Assessment Answers   **181**

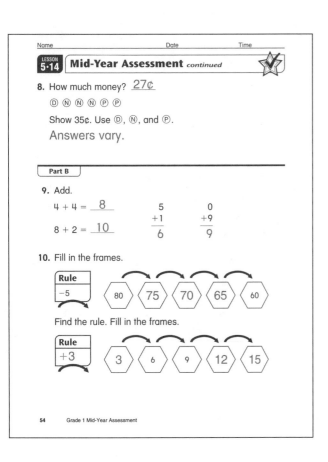

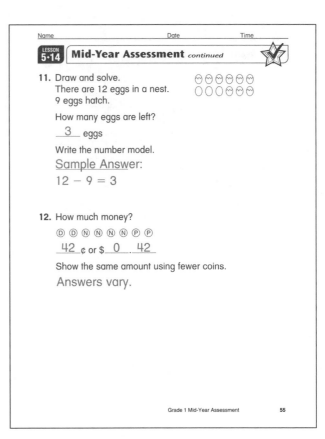

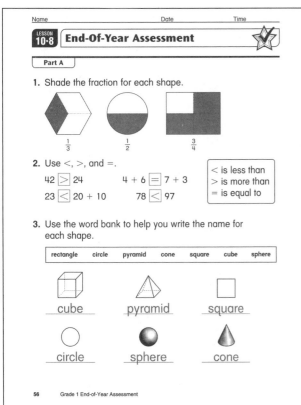

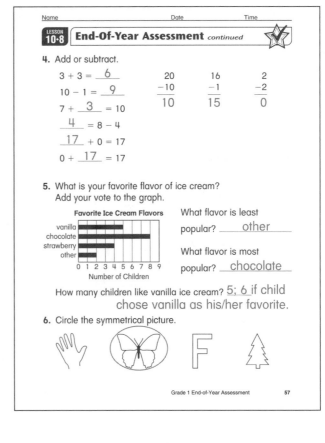

Panel 1 (top-left):

Name   Date   Time

LESSON 5·14 **Mid-Year Assessment** *continued*

8. How much money? _27¢_

Ⓓ Ⓝ Ⓝ Ⓝ Ⓟ Ⓟ

Show 35¢. Use Ⓓ, Ⓝ, and Ⓟ.

Answers vary.

Part B

9. Add.

$4 + 4 =$ _8_   5   0
                   +1   +9
$8 + 2 =$ _10_   ___   ___
                    6   9

10. Fill in the frames.

Rule
−5

80 75 70 65 60

Find the rule. Fill in the frames.

Rule
+3

3 6 9 12 15

54   Grade 1 Mid-Year Assessment

Panel 2 (top-right):

Name   Date   Time

LESSON 5·14 **Mid-Year Assessment** *continued*

11. Draw and solve.
There are 12 eggs in a nest.
9 eggs hatch.

How many eggs are left?

_3_ eggs

Write the number model.

Sample Answer:
$12 − 9 = 3$

12. How much money?

Ⓓ Ⓓ Ⓝ Ⓝ Ⓝ Ⓟ Ⓟ

_42_ ¢ or $ _0_ . _42_

Show the same amount using fewer coins.

Answers vary.

Grade 1 Mid-Year Assessment   55

Panel 3 (bottom-left):

Name   Date   Time

LESSON 10·8 **End-Of-Year Assessment**

Part A

1. Shade the fraction for each shape.

$\frac{1}{3}$ $\frac{1}{2}$ $\frac{3}{4}$

2. Use <, >, and =.

42 > 24	4 + 6 = 7 + 3
23 < 20 + 10	78 < 97

< is less than
> is more than
= is equal to

3. Use the word bank to help you write the name for each shape.

| rectangle | circle | pyramid | cone | square | cube | sphere |

cube   pyramid   square

circle   sphere   cone

56   Grade 1 End-of-Year Assessment

Panel 4 (bottom-right):

Name   Date   Time

LESSON 10·8 **End-Of-Year Assessment** *continued*

4. Add or subtract.

$3 + 3 =$ _6_   20   16   2
                    −10   −1   −2
$10 − 1 =$ _9_   ___   ___   ___
                     10   15   0
$7 +$ _3_ $= 10$

_4_ $= 8 − 4$

_17_ $+ 0 = 17$

$0 +$ _17_ $= 17$

5. What is your favorite flavor of ice cream?
Add your vote to the graph.

Favorite Ice Cream Flavors

vanilla
chocolate
strawberry
other

0 1 2 3 4 5 6 7 8 9
Number of Children

What flavor is least popular? _other_

What flavor is most popular? _chocolate_

How many children like vanilla ice cream? _5; 6_ if child chose vanilla as his/her favorite.

6. Circle the symmetrical picture.

Grade 1 End-of-Year Assessment   57

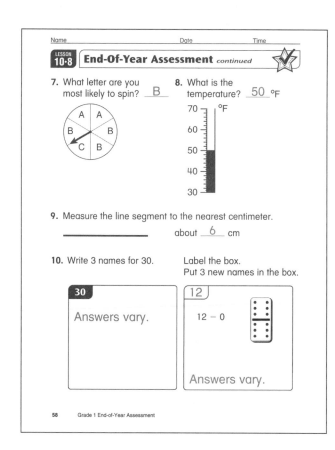

LESSON 10·8 End-Of-Year Assessment *continued*

7. What letter are you most likely to spin? __B__

8. What is the temperature? __50__ °F

9. Measure the line segment to the nearest centimeter.

about __6__ cm

10. Write 3 names for 30.

30
Answers vary.

Label the box.
Put 3 new names in the box.

12
12 − 0
Answers vary.

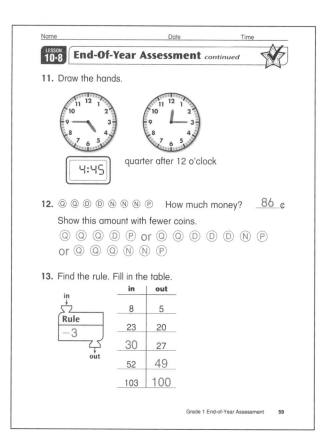

LESSON 10·8 End-Of-Year Assessment *continued*

11. Draw the hands.

4:45   quarter after 12 o'clock

12. Ⓠ Ⓠ Ⓓ Ⓓ Ⓝ Ⓝ Ⓝ Ⓟ   How much money? __86__ ¢

Show this amount with fewer coins.

Ⓠ Ⓠ Ⓠ Ⓓ Ⓟ or Ⓠ Ⓠ Ⓓ Ⓓ Ⓝ Ⓟ
or Ⓠ Ⓠ Ⓠ Ⓝ Ⓝ Ⓟ

13. Find the rule. Fill in the table.

Rule −3

in	out
8	5
23	20
30	27
52	49
103	100

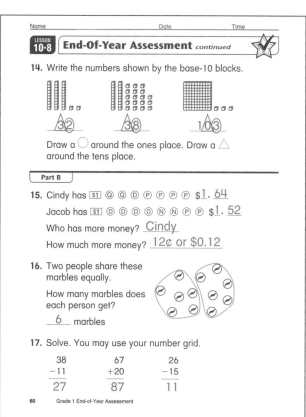

LESSON 10·8 End-Of-Year Assessment *continued*

14. Write the numbers shown by the base-10 blocks.

△3Ⓞ2   △3Ⓞ8   1△0Ⓞ3

Draw a Ⓞ around the ones place. Draw a △ around the tens place.

Part B

15. Cindy has $1 Ⓠ Ⓠ Ⓓ Ⓟ Ⓟ Ⓟ Ⓟ $1.__64__

Jacob has $1 Ⓓ Ⓓ Ⓓ Ⓝ Ⓝ Ⓟ Ⓟ $1.__52__

Who has more money? __Cindy__

How much more money? __12¢ or $0.12__

16. Two people share these marbles equally.

How many marbles does each person get?

__6__ marbles

17. Solve. You may use your number grid.

38	67	26
−11	+20	−15
27	87	11

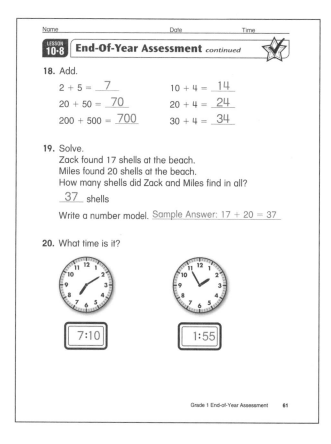

LESSON 10·8 End-Of-Year Assessment *continued*

18. Add.

2 + 5 = __7__   10 + 4 = __14__

20 + 50 = __70__   20 + 4 = __24__

200 + 500 = __700__   30 + 4 = __34__

19. Solve.
Zack found 17 shells at the beach.
Miles found 20 shells at the beach.
How many shells did Zack and Miles find in all?

__37__ shells

Write a number model. __Sample Answer: 17 + 20 = 37__

20. What time is it?

7:10   1:55

Page 62

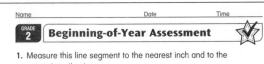
GRADE 2 Beginning-of-Year Assessment

1. Measure this line segment to the nearest inch and to the nearest centimeter.

   <u>5</u> inches   <u>12</u> centimeters

2. Complete the bar graph.
   Lee has 3 stickers.
   Joe has 6 stickers.
   Ivan has 4 stickers.
   Mia has 4 stickers.

   Number of Stickers

   a. Maximum number of stickers:
      <u>6</u>

   b. Minimum number of stickers:
      <u>3</u>

   c. Median number of stickers:
      <u>4</u>

   d. Mode number of stickers: <u>4</u>

3. Color $\frac{3}{4}$.

4. What fraction of the circles is shaded? $\frac{4}{5}$ or $\frac{8}{10}$

Page 63

GRADE 2 Beginning-of-Year Assessment *cont.*

5. Shade $\frac{1}{2}$ and write the fraction.

   $\frac{1}{2}$ or $\frac{4}{8}$

6. Fill in the oval next to the best estimate.

   a. 322 + 283 is about
      ○ 400
      ○ 500
      ● 600

   b. 89 − 52 is about
      ○ 30
      ● 40
      ○ 50

7. The area of the square is <u>9</u> square centimeters.

8. Use counters, a number grid, or pictures to find the answer.

   Unit

   a. 58
      +65
      ‾‾‾
      123

   b. 27
      +44
      ‾‾‾
      71

   c. 74
      −48
      ‾‾‾
      26

   d. 62
      −37
      ‾‾‾
      25

Page 64

GRADE 2 Beginning-of-Year Assessment *cont.*

9. Write the time.

   a.
   b.
   c.

   10 : 55   8 : 35   4 : 10

10. Complete.

    1 day = <u>24</u> hours   1 week = <u>7</u> days
    1 minute = <u>60</u> seconds   1 hour = <u>60</u> minutes

11. Use counters or drawings to solve.

    a. 12 pencils. 4 children.
    How many pencils per child? <u>3</u> pencils

    b. 60 raisins. 6 raisins per child.
    How many children? <u>10</u> children

12. Complete the diagram. Use counters to solve.

    a. 6 bikes. Each bike has 2 wheels. How many wheels in all? <u>12</u>

bikes	wheels per bike	wheels in all
6	2	12

Page 65

GRADE 2 Beginning-of-Year Assessment *cont.*

   b. 8 children. Each child has 2 apples.
   How many apples in all? <u>16</u>

children	apples per child	apples in all
8	2	16

13. Use =, +, or −.

    a. 6 [+] 7 = 13
    b. 12 [−] 2 = 10
    c. 22 [=] 10 + 12
    d. 16 = 10 [+] 6
    e. 7 [−] 3 = 4
    f. 30 = 50 [−] 20

Use bills and coins to solve.

14. Max saved $5.40 for his class field trip. His friend saved $3.50. How much money did they save in all?
    Write a number model.
    a. Answer: <u>$8.90</u>
    b. Number model: $5.40 + $3.50 = $8.90

15. Isabel bought 1 pen for $0.85. She paid with $1.00. How much change did Isabel get back? <u>$0.15</u>

---

184   Grade 2 Assessment Answers

Page 66 (top left)

Name   Date   Time

GRADE 2 **Beginning-of-Year Assessment** *cont.*

16. Write the fact family for 9, 4, and 36.

$$\underline{9} \times \underline{4} = 36 \qquad \underline{4} \times \underline{9} = 36$$
$$\underline{36} \div \underline{9} = \underline{4} \qquad \underline{36} \div \underline{4} = \underline{9}$$

17. Solve.

$6 \times 8 = \underline{48}$ $8 \times 4 = \underline{32}$
$7 \times 3 = \underline{21}$ $7 \times 6 = \underline{42}$
$9 \times 6 = \underline{54}$ $9 \times 3 = \underline{27}$

18. Solve.

a. If   (trapezoid)   is ONE, then   (triangle)   is $\underline{\tfrac{1}{3}}$.

b. If   (triangle)   is ONE, then   (hexagon)   is $\underline{6}$.

66   Grade 2 Beginning-of-Year Assessment

Page 67 (top right)

Name   Date   Time

GRADE 2 **Beginning-of-Year Assessment** *cont.*

19. Kathy bought juice for $1.81. She paid with $2.00. How much change does Kathy get?

Answer: $\underline{\$0.19}$

20. Solve. Show your work.

a. $67 + 26 = \underline{93}$ **b.** $218 + 159 = \underline{377}$ **c.** $86 - 37 = \underline{49}$ **d.** $115 - 27 = \underline{88}$ **e.** $172 - 138 = \underline{34}$

21. Find the area.

$\underline{10}$ square centimeters

22. Write the number that is 10,000 less and 10,000 more.

Less		More
236	10,236	20,236
4,872	14,872	24,872
143,234	153,234	163,234

Grade 2 Beginning-of-Year Assessment   67

Page 68 (bottom left)

Name   Date   Time

LESSON 6·11 **Mid-Year Assessment**

Part A

1. Draw line segment $\overline{AB}$.

A   B

2. Circle the pair of line segments that are parallel.

3. The temperature is $\underline{42}$ °F.

4. Write the fact family for 2, 11, and 9.

$$2 + 9 = 11$$
$$9 + 2 = 11$$
$$11 - 2 = 9$$
$$11 - 9 = 2$$

5. Use <, >, or =.

$462 \underline{<} 624$
$209 \underline{<} 2{,}009$
$8 + 5 \underline{>} 7 + 5$
$9 + 6 \underline{=} 8 + 7$

6. Fill in the missing numbers.

88		
98	99	
108	109	110
118		

68   Grade 2 Mid-Year Assessment

Page 69 (bottom right)

Name   Date   Time

LESSON 6·11 **Mid-Year Assessment** *continued*

7. This shape is a
○ hexagon.
○ rhombus.
○ trapezoid.

8. This is a picture of a
○ pyramid.
● cylinder.
○ rectangular prism.

9. Draw the hour and minute hands to show 6:45.

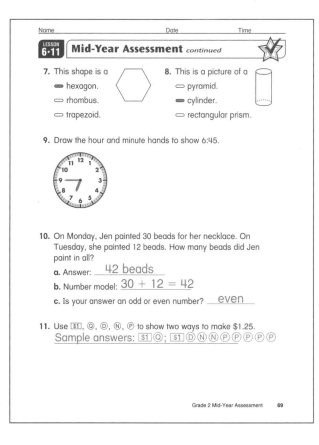

10. On Monday, Jen painted 30 beads for her necklace. On Tuesday, she painted 12 beads. How many beads did Jen paint in all?

a. Answer: $\underline{42 \text{ beads}}$
b. Number model: $\underline{30 + 12 = 42}$
c. Is your answer an odd or even number? $\underline{\text{even}}$

11. Use $1, Q, D, N, P to show two ways to make $1.25.

Sample answers: $1 Q; $1 D N P P P P P

Grade 2 Mid-Year Assessment   69

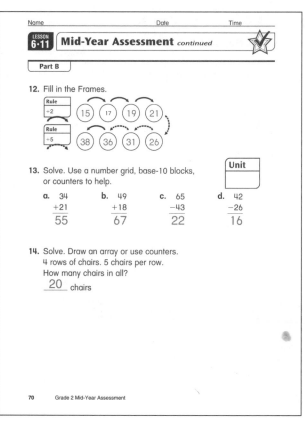

LESSON 6·11 **Mid-Year Assessment** *continued*

Part B

12. Fill in the Frames.

Rule +2
15   17   19   21

Rule +5
38   36   31   26

13. Solve. Use a number grid, base-10 blocks, or counters to help.

Unit

a. 34
+21
55

b. 49
+18
67

c. 65
−43
22

d. 42
−26
16

14. Solve. Draw an array or use counters.
4 rows of chairs. 5 chairs per row.
How many chairs in all?
20 chairs

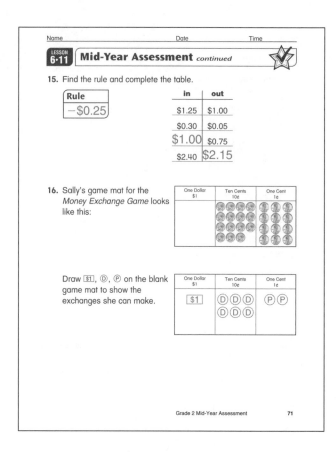

LESSON 6·11 **Mid-Year Assessment** *continued*

15. Find the rule and complete the table.

Rule
−$0.25

in	out
$1.25	$1.00
$0.30	$0.05
$1.00	$0.75
$2.40	$2.15

16. Sally's game mat for the *Money Exchange Game* looks like this:

Draw $1, D, P on the blank game mat to show the exchanges she can make.

One Dollar $1	Ten Cents 10¢	One Cent 1¢
$1	D D D D D D	P P

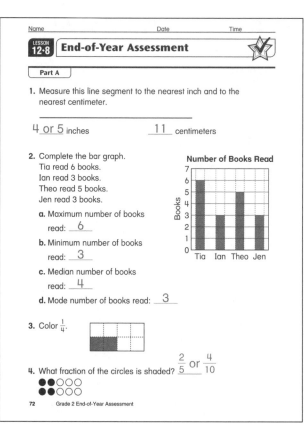

LESSON 12·8 **End-of-Year Assessment**

Part A

1. Measure this line segment to the nearest inch and to the nearest centimeter.

4 or 5 inches   **11** centimeters

2. Complete the bar graph.
Tia read 6 books.
Ian read 3 books.
Theo read 5 books.
Jen read 3 books.

Number of Books Read

a. Maximum number of books
read: **6**

b. Minimum number of books
read: **3**

c. Median number of books
read: **4**

d. Mode number of books read: **3**

3. Color $\frac{1}{4}$.

4. What fraction of the circles is shaded? $\frac{2}{5}$ or $\frac{4}{10}$
● ● ○ ○ ○
● ● ○ ○ ○

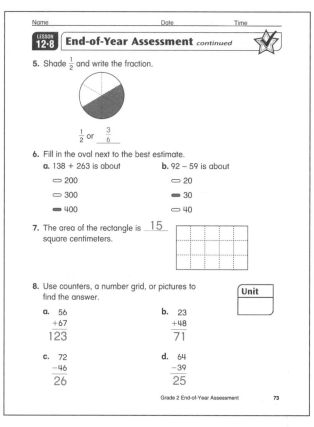

LESSON 12·8 **End-of-Year Assessment** *continued*

5. Shade $\frac{1}{2}$ and write the fraction.

$\frac{1}{2}$ or $\frac{3}{6}$

6. Fill in the oval next to the best estimate.
a. 138 + 263 is about
◯ 200
◯ 300
⬛ 400

b. 92 − 59 is about
◯ 20
⬛ 30
◯ 40

7. The area of the rectangle is **15** square centimeters.

8. Use counters, a number grid, or pictures to find the answer.

Unit

a. 56
+67
123

b. 23
+48
71

c. 72
−46
26

d. 64
−39
25

LESSON 12·8 | **End-of-Year Assessment** *continued*

9. Write the time.

a.   **b.**   **c.**

8 : 05   4 : 25   11 : 50

10. Complete.

1 week = __7__ days   1 day = __24__ hours

1 hour = __60__ minutes   1 minute = __60__ seconds

11. Use counters or drawings to solve.

a. 15 stickers. 3 children.

How many stickers per child? __5__ stickers

b. 40 candies. 4 candies per child.

How many children? __10__ children

12. Complete the diagram. Use counters to solve.

a. 5 cars. Each car has 4 wheels. How many wheels in all? __20__

cars	wheels per car	wheels in all
5	4	20

LESSON 12·8 | **End-of-Year Assessment** *continued*

b. 6 children. Each child has 3 cookies.

How many cookies in all? __18__

children	cookies per child	cookies in all
6	3	18

13. Use =, +, or −.

a. 8 $\boxed{+}$ 6 = 14   **b.** 15 $\boxed{-}$ 5 = 10

c. 25 $\boxed{=}$ 15 + 10   **d.** 18 = 10 $\boxed{+}$ 8

e. 9 $\boxed{-}$ 3 = 6   **f.** 20 = 40 $\boxed{-}$ 20

Use bills and coins to solve.

14. Ian saved $4.50 for his mother's birthday present. His sister saved $3.40. How much money did they save in all? Write a number model.

a. Answer: __$7.90__

b. Number model: __$4.50 + $3.40 = $7.90__

15. Carlos bought 1 pencil for $0.65. He paid with $1.00. How much change did Carlos get back? __$0.35__

LESSON 12·8 | **End-of-Year Assessment** *continued*

Part B

16. Write the fact family for 8, 4, and 32.

$$\frac{8}{} \times \frac{4}{} = \frac{32}{} \qquad \frac{4}{} \times \frac{8}{} = \frac{32}{}$$

$$\frac{32}{} \div \frac{4}{} = \frac{8}{} \qquad \frac{32}{} \div \frac{8}{} = \frac{4}{}$$

17. Solve.

$6 \times 7 = $ __42__ $8 \times 6 = $ __48__

$9 \times 3 = $ __27__ $7 \times 4 = $ __28__

$9 \times 7 = $ __63__ $6 \times 6 = $ __36__

18. Solve.

a. If 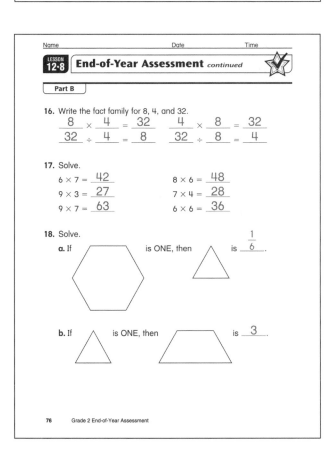 is ONE, then is __$\frac{1}{6}$__.

b. If is ONE, then is __3__.

LESSON 12·8 | **End-of-Year Assessment** *continued*

19. Caitlin bought yogurt for $1.72. She paid with $2.00. How much change does Caitlin get?

Answer: __$0.28__

20. Solve. Show your work.

a.	**b.**	**c.**	**d.**	**e.**
65	238	84	113	154
+28	+149	−38	−25	−126
93	387	46	88	28

21. Find the area.

 __8__ square centimeters

22. Write the number that is 10,000 less and 10,000 more.

Less		More
458	10,458	20,458
2,964	12,964	22,964
151,324	161,324	171,324

Grade 2 Assessment Answers   **187**

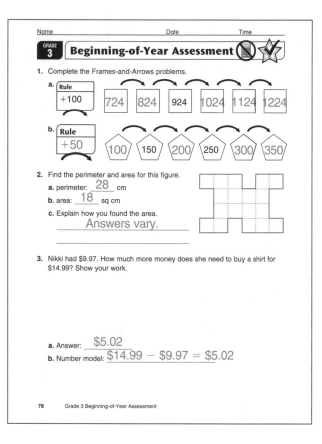

GRADE 3 **Beginning-of-Year Assessment**

1. Complete the Frames-and-Arrows problems.

   a. **Rule** +100
   724 824 924 1024 1124 1224

   b. **Rule** +50
   100 150 200 250 300 350

2. Find the perimeter and area for this figure.
   a. perimeter: 28 cm
   b. area: 18 sq cm
   c. Explain how you found the area.
   Answers vary.

3. Nikki had $9.97. How much more money does she need to buy a shirt for $14.99? Show your work.

   a. Answer: $5.02
   b. Number model: $14.99 − $9.97 = $5.02

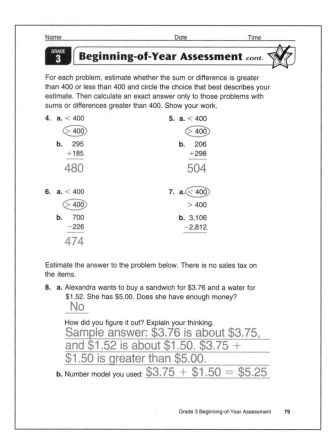

GRADE 3 **Beginning-of-Year Assessment** *cont.*

For each problem, estimate whether the sum or difference is greater than 400 or less than 400 and circle the choice that best describes your estimate. Then calculate an exact answer only to those problems with sums or differences greater than 400. Show your work.

4. a. < 400
   (> 400)
   b. 295
      +185
      480

5. a. < 400
   (> 400)
   b. 206
      +298
      504

6. a. < 400
   (> 400)
   b. 700
      −226
      474

7. a. (< 400)
   > 400
   b. 3,106
      −2,812

Estimate the answer to the problem below. There is no sales tax on the items.

8. a. Alexandra wants to buy a sandwich for $3.76 and a water for $1.52. She has $5.00. Does she have enough money?
   No

   How did you figure it out? Explain your thinking.
   Sample answer: $3.76 is about $3.75, and $1.52 is about $1.50. $3.75 + $1.50 is greater than $5.00.

   b. Number model you used: $3.75 + $1.50 = $5.25

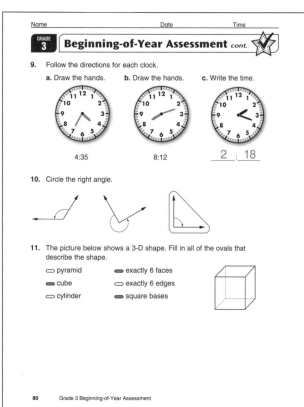

GRADE 3 **Beginning-of-Year Assessment** *cont.*

9. Follow the directions for each clock.

   a. Draw the hands.   b. Draw the hands.   c. Write the time.

   4:35   8:12   2 : 18

10. Circle the right angle.

11. The picture below shows a 3-D shape. Fill in all of the ovals that describe the shape.
    ○ pyramid   ● exactly 6 faces
    ● cube   ○ exactly 6 edges
    ○ cylinder   ● square bases

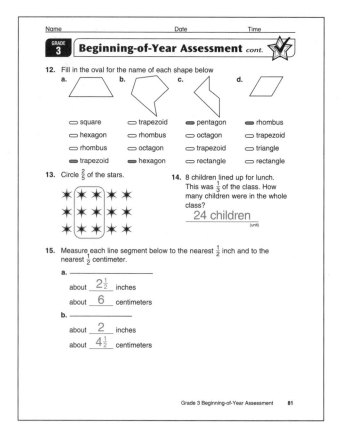

GRADE 3 **Beginning-of-Year Assessment** *cont.*

12. Fill in the oval for the name of each shape below
    a.   b.   c.   d.

    ○ square   ○ trapezoid   ● pentagon   ● rhombus
    ○ hexagon   ○ rhombus   ○ octagon   ○ trapezoid
    ○ rhombus   ○ octagon   ○ trapezoid   ○ triangle
    ● trapezoid   ● hexagon   ○ rectangle   ○ rectangle

13. Circle $\frac{2}{5}$ of the stars.

    ✳ ✳ ✳ ✳ ✳
    ✳ ✳ ✳ ✳ ✳
    ✳ ✳ ✳ ✳ ✳

14. 8 children lined up for lunch. This was $\frac{1}{3}$ of the class. How many children were in the whole class?
    24 children
    (unit)

15. Measure each line segment below to the nearest $\frac{1}{2}$ inch and to the nearest $\frac{1}{2}$ centimeter.
    a. _____
    about 2$\frac{1}{2}$ inches
    about 6 centimeters
    b. _____
    about 2 inches
    about 4$\frac{1}{2}$ centimeters

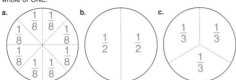

GRADE 3 **Beginning-of-Year Assessment** *cont.*

16. Write the fraction in each separate area. The circle represents the whole or ONE.

a.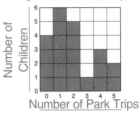

$\frac{1}{8}$ $\frac{1}{8}$
$\frac{1}{8}$ $\frac{1}{8}$
$\frac{1}{8}$ $\frac{1}{8}$
$\frac{1}{8}$ $\frac{1}{8}$

b. $\frac{1}{2}$ $\frac{1}{2}$

c. $\frac{1}{3}$ $\frac{1}{3}$ $\frac{1}{3}$

17. Marissa took a survey to find the number of times her friends went to the park in a week. She recorded the following data:

Make a bar graph to show her survey results. Remember to add labels and a title.

Number of Park Trips	Number of Children
0	////
1	///// /
2	/////
3	/
4	///
5	//

Title: **My Friends' Park Trips**

Number of Children (vertical axis)
Number of Park Trips (horizontal axis)

18. Use the data in the tally chart and bar graph to fill in the blanks.

a. maximum **5**   **c.** range **5**

b. minimum **0**   **d.** median **2**

GRADE 3 **Beginning-of-Year Assessment** *cont.*

19. Use your favorite multiplication method to solve. Show your work.

a. 62
 × 8
496

b. 308
 × 6
1,848

20. Juan bought 6 boxes of straws on sale. There were 9 straws in each box. How many straws did he buy altogether?

a. Answer: **54**   **b.** Number model: **$6 \times 9 = 54$**

21. Complete the "What's My Rule?" tables and write the rules.

a. Rule **×4**

in	out
8	32
9	36
20	80
25	**100**

b. Rule **−8**

in	out
94	**86**
60	52
81	73
6	−2

c. Rule **×8**

in	out
5	40
7	56
10	80
60	**480**

Answers vary. **Answers vary.** **Answers vary.**

GRADE 3 **Beginning-of-Year Assessment** *cont.*

22. Fill in the missing number in the Fact Triangle.

5,600
×, ÷
8   **700**

23. Write the fact family for the Fact Triangle.

$8 \times 700 = 5,600$
$700 \times 8 = 5,600$
$5,600 \div 700 = 8$
$5,600 \div 8 = 700$

24. On the top edge of the ruler below, label each mark with the letter listed.

A: $\frac{1}{4}$ in.   **B:** $3\frac{3}{8}$ in.   **C:** $1\frac{3}{4}$ in.   **D:** $4\frac{1}{8}$ in.

A   C   B   D

Inches (in.)

25. How far is it from point *A* to point *C* in Problem 24? **$1\frac{1}{2}$ inches**

26. Put in parentheses to make each number sentence true.

a. $(3 \times 20) + 9 = 69$ **c.** $60 + (40 \times 10) = 460$

b. $128 = (40 \times 3) + 8$ **d.** $2,397 = (30 \times 80) - 3$

GRADE 3 **Beginning-of-Year Assessment** *cont.*

27. The children in the Cooking Club baked 31 pretzels. They gave each teacher 4 pretzels. How many teachers received pretzels? How many pretzels were left over? Show your work.

a. Answer: **7 teachers received pretzels.**
3 pretzels were left over.

b. Number model: **$31 \div 4 = 7 R3$**

28. Solve. Use your favorite multiplication method. Show your work.

a. 17
 ×23
391

b. 29
 ×56
1,624

LESSON 6·13 Mid-Year Assessment

Part A

1.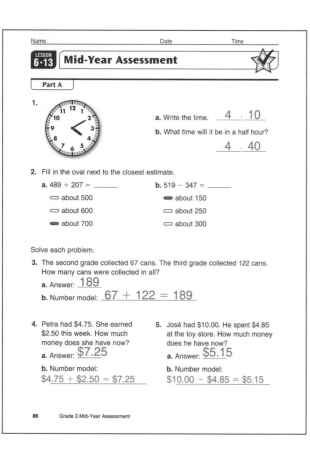

   a. Write the time. **4 : 10**

   b. What time will it be in a half hour?
   4 : 40

2. Fill in the oval next to the closest estimate.

   a. 489 + 207 = _____

   - about 500
   - about 600
   - ● about 700

   b. 519 − 347 = _____

   - ● about 150
   - about 250
   - about 300

Solve each problem.

3. The second grade collected 67 cans. The third grade collected 122 cans. How many cans were collected in all?

   a. Answer: **189**

   b. Number model: **67 + 122 = 189**

4. Petra had $4.75. She earned $2.50 this week. How much money does she have now?

   a. Answer: **$7.25**

   b. Number model:
   $4.75 + $2.50 = $7.25

5. José had $10.00. He spent $4.85 at the toy store. How much money does he have now?

   a. Answer: **$5.15**

   b. Number model:
   $10.00 − $4.85 = $5.15

LESSON 6·13 Mid-Year Assessment *continued*

6. 4 children
   7 pencils per child
   How many pencils in all?

   a. **28** pencils

   b. Number model: **4 × 7 = 28**

children	pencils per child	pencils in all
4	7	?

7. 20 books shared by 4 children. How many books per child?

   a. **5** books

   b. Number model:
   4 × 5 = 20 or 20 ÷ 4 = 5

children	books per child	books in all
4	?	20

8. Fill in the unit box. Complete each fact.

   a. 7 + 8 = **15**

   b. 5 + **6** = 11

   c. 6 + 7 = **13**

   d. 9 = 15 − **6**

   e. 4 + **6** = 10

   f. **16** = 9 + 7

   Unit

9. Fill in the unit box. Use >, <, or =.

   a. 305 **<** 350

   b. 160 **<** 1,006

   c. 40,007 **>** 4,000.9

   d. 729 **<** 927

   e. 38.2 **<** 38.8

   f. 300 + 400 **=** 900 − 200

   Unit

10. Circle every digit in the tenths place in problem 9.

11. Write the smallest 6-digit number you can make with the digits 7, 3, 4, 8, 2, and 9.
    234,789

LESSON 6·13 Mid-Year Assessment *continued*

12. Fill in the unit box. Add or subtract. Show your work.

    a. 682
       − 236
       446

    b. 427
       + 339
       766

    Unit

13. Complete the Frames-and-Arrows puzzles.

    a.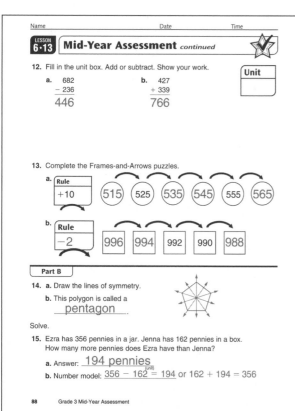

    Rule +10
    515 525 **535** **545** 555 565

    b. Rule −2
    996 994 992 990 **988**

Part B

14. a. Draw the lines of symmetry.

    b. This polygon is called a
    pentagon.

Solve.

15. Ezra has 356 pennies in a jar. Jenna has 162 pennies in a box. How many more pennies does Ezra have than Jenna?

    a. Answer: **194 pennies** (unit)

    b. Number model: **356 − 162 = 194 or 162 + 194 = 356**

LESSON 6·13 Mid-Year Assessment *continued*

16. Fill in the unit box. Solve each problem. Show your work.

    a. 2,391
       + 4,489
       6,880

    b. 6,704
       − 3,842
       2,862

    Unit

17. Write the letter for the best description of each event.

    b A coin will land HEADS-up.

    a It will rain at least once this year.

    c The sun will rise tomorrow.

    d A bird will fly into your house.

    a. likely
    b. 50-50
    c. sure
    d. unlikely

18. Find the rule and complete the table.

    Rule ×8

in	out
3	**24**
2	16
4	**32**
8	64

    Answers vary

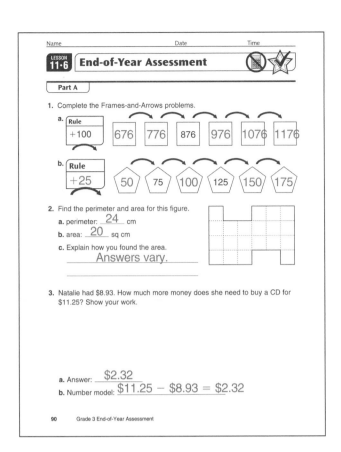

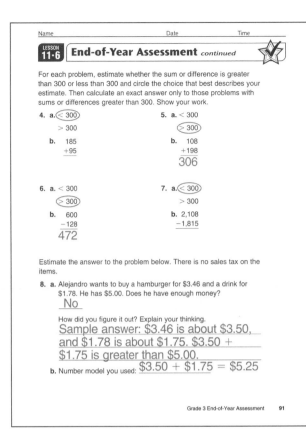

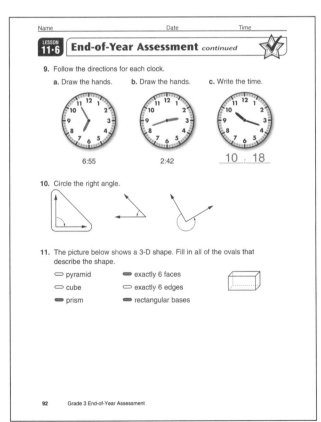

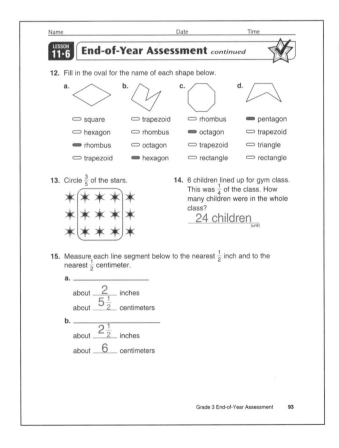

Top Left Panel

LESSON 11·6 **End-of-Year Assessment** *continued*

16. Write the fraction in each separate area. The hexagon represents the whole or ONE.

a.
$\frac{1}{3}$ $\frac{1}{3}$
$\frac{1}{3}$

b.
$\frac{1}{6}$ $\frac{1}{6}$
$\frac{1}{6}$ $\frac{1}{6}$
$\frac{1}{6}$ $\frac{1}{6}$

c.
$\frac{1}{2}$ $\frac{1}{2}$

17. Serita took a survey to find the number of times her friends visited the public library in a month. She recorded the following data:

Make a bar graph to show her survey results. Remember to add labels and a title.

Number of Library Visits	Number of Children
0	//
1	////
2	///// /
3	/////
4	//
5	/

Title: My Friends' Library Visits

Number of Children (y-axis)
Number of Library Visits (x-axis)

18. Use the data in the tally chart and bar graph to fill in the blanks.

a. maximum __5__   c. range __5__
b. minimum __0__   d. median __2__

Top Right Panel

LESSON 11·6 **End-of-Year Assessment** *continued*

19. Use your favorite multiplication method to solve. Show your work.

a. 74
×6
444

b. 406
× 5
2,030

20. Julia bought 7 boxes of pencils on sale. There were 8 pencils in each box. How many pencils did she buy altogether?

a. Answer: __56__   b. Number model: $7 \times 8 = 56$

21. Complete the "What's My Rule?" tables and write the rules.

a.
Rule ×3

in	out
7	21
8	24
30	90
25	75

b.
Rule −10

in	out
82	72
43	33
75	65
5	−5

c.
Rule ×6

in	out
8	48
9	54
10	60
70	420

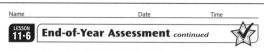

Answers vary.   Answers vary.   Answers vary.

Bottom Left Panel

LESSON 11·6 **End-of-Year Assessment** *continued*

Part B

22. Fill in the missing number in the Fact Triangle.

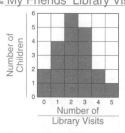
4,800
×, ÷
8   600

23. Write the fact family for the Fact Triangle.

$8 \times 600 = 4,800$
$600 \times 8 = 4,800$
$4,800 \div 600 = 8$
$4,800 \div 8 = 600$

24. On the top edge of the ruler below, label each mark with the letter listed.

A: $\frac{3}{4}$ in.   B: $4\frac{7}{8}$ in.   C: $1\frac{1}{4}$ in.   D: $2\frac{5}{8}$ in.

A C   D   B
0 1 2 3 4 5 6
Inches (in.)

25. How far is it from point A to point C in Problem 24? $\frac{1}{2}$ inch

26. Put in parentheses to make each number sentence true.

a. $(2 \times 40) + 7 = 87$ c. $50 + (50 \times 10) = 550$
b. $124 = (60 \times 2) + 4$ d. $4,499 = (50 \times 90) - 1$

Bottom Right Panel

LESSON 11·6 **End-of-Year Assessment** *continued*

27. The children in the Garden Club picked 29 flowers. They gave each teacher 3 flowers. How many teachers received flowers? How many flowers were left over? Show your work.

9 teachers received flowers.
a. Answer: 2 flowers were left over.
b. Number model: $29 \div 3 = 9R2$

28. Solve. Use your favorite multiplication method. Show your work.

a. 15
×21
315

b. 39
×58
2,262

GRADE 4 | **Beginning-of-Year Assessment**

1. Complete.

a. $\frac{1}{4}$ of 24 = **6**

b. 5 = $\frac{1}{4}$ of **20**

c. **15** = $\frac{5}{7}$ of 21

d. 12 = $\frac{3}{4}$ of **16**

e. $\frac{7}{5}$ of 25 = **35**

f. $\frac{3}{2}$ of **14** = 21

2. Is 129 a multiple of 6? **No**

How do you know? **It is not divided evenly by 6.**

3. Is 6 a factor of 78? **Yes**

How do you know? **6 * 13 = 78**

4. Write each fraction as a decimal and as a percent.

a. $\frac{22}{100}$ = **0** . **22** = **22** %

b. $\frac{9}{10}$ = **0** . **9** = **90** %

c. $\frac{1}{4}$ = **0** . **25** = **25** %

d. $\frac{3}{5}$ = **0** . **6** = **60** %

e. $\frac{4}{100}$ = **0** . **04** = **4** %

f. $\frac{20}{10}$ = **2** . **0** = **200** %

5. Insert >, <, or = to make each number sentence true.

a. $\frac{3}{7}$ **<** $\frac{4}{7}$

b. $\frac{1}{3}$ **>** $\frac{1}{5}$

c. $\frac{3}{4}$ **<** $\frac{6}{7}$

d. Explain how you solved Problem 5c.

Sample answer: $\frac{6}{7}$ is closer to 1 than $\frac{3}{4}$ so $\frac{6}{7}$ is larger than $\frac{3}{4}$.

GRADE 4 | **Beginning-of-Year Assessment** *cont.*

6. Order the fractions from smallest to largest.

$\frac{1}{6}$, $\frac{3}{4}$, $\frac{1}{5}$, $\frac{24}{25}$, $\frac{4}{9}$

$\frac{1}{6}$ $\frac{1}{5}$ $\frac{4}{9}$ $\frac{3}{4}$ $\frac{24}{25}$
smallest   largest

7. Multiply or divide. Show your work.

a. 35 * 43 = **1,505**

b. **6,384** = 76 * 84

c. **83** = 664 / 8

d. 748 ÷ 5 = **149 R3**

8. Add or subtract.

a. $\frac{2}{7} + \frac{3}{7}$ = **$\frac{5}{7}$**

b. $\frac{1}{4} + \frac{2}{8}$ = **$\frac{2}{4}$ or $\frac{1}{2}$**

c. **$\frac{4}{6}$ or $\frac{2}{3}$** = $\frac{5}{6} - \frac{1}{6}$

d. **$\frac{1}{4}$** = $\frac{3}{4} - \frac{1}{2}$

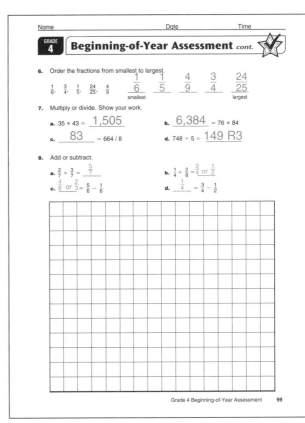

GRADE 4 | **Beginning-of-Year Assessment** *cont.*

9. The table shows the number of people who attended a play each week during its run. Create a line graph to show the data. Use a straightedge to connect the data points. Label each axis and include a title.

Week	Number of People
1	300
2	250
3	150
4	100
5	150
6	100
7	100
8	50

10. Use the following terms to complete the statements below.

impossible
likely
unlikely
very likely

a. It is **unlikely** that the spinner will land on 1.

b. It is **very likely** that the spinner will land on a number not equal to 1.

c. It is **impossible** that the spinner will land on a number less than $\frac{7}{8}$.

d. It is **likely** that the spinner will land on a number less than or equal to 4.

GRADE 4 | **Beginning-of-Year Assessment** *cont.*

11. Complete.

a. Color $\frac{3}{4}$ of the spinner at the right.

b. What fraction of the spinner is *not* colored? **$\frac{1}{4}$**

c. What *percent* of the spinner is colored? **75%**

d. If you spin the spinner 100 times, about how many times would you expect it to land on the colored part? **75** times

e. If you spin the spinner 400 times, about how many times would you expect it to land on the colored part? **300** times

12. Use these formulas to calculate the areas of the figures below.

Rectangle	Parallelogram	Triangle
Area = base * height	Area = base * height	Area = $\frac{1}{2}$ * (base * height)

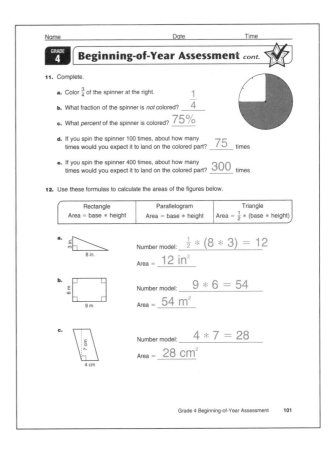

a.

Number model: **$\frac{1}{2} * (8 * 3) = 12$**

Area = **12 in^2**

b.

Number model: **9 * 6 = 54**

Area = **54 m^2**

c.

Number model: **4 * 7 = 28**

Area = **28 cm^2**

Grade 4 Assessment Answers   **193**

13. Calculate the volume of each rectangular prism.

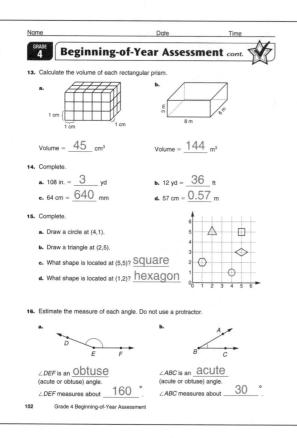

a.

1 cm

1 cm   1 cm

Volume = __45__ cm³

b.

3 m

8 m   6 m

Volume = __144__ m³

14. Complete.

a. 108 in. = __3__ yd

b. 12 yd = __36__ ft

c. 64 cm = __640__ mm

d. 57 cm = __0.57__ m

15. Complete.

a. Draw a circle at (4,1).

b. Draw a triangle at (2,5).

c. What shape is located at (5,5)? __square__

d. What shape is located at (1,2)? __hexagon__

16. Estimate the measure of each angle. Do not use a protractor.

a.

D   E   F

∠DEF is an __obtuse__
(acute or obtuse) angle.

∠DEF measures about __160__ °.

b.

A
B   C

∠ABC is an __acute__
(acute or obtuse) angle.

∠ABC measures about __30__ °.

---

17. The objects below have the shapes of geometric solids. Name the solids.

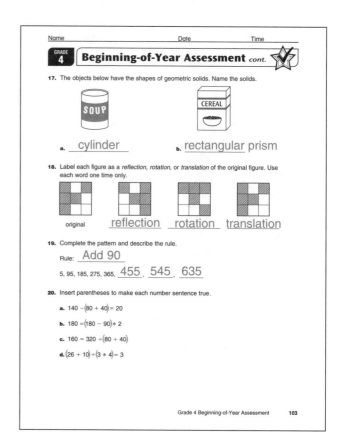

SOUP

CEREAL

a. __cylinder__

b. __rectangular__ prism

18. Label each figure as a *reflection*, *rotation*, or *translation* of the original figure. Use each word one time only.

original   __reflection__   __rotation__   __translation__

19. Complete the pattern and describe the rule.

Rule: __Add 90__

5, 95, 185, 275, 365, __455__, __545__, __635__

20. Insert parentheses to make each number sentence true.

a. 140 − (80 + 40) = 20

b. 180 = (180 − 90) ∗ 2

c. 160 = 320 ÷ (80 + 40)

d. (26 + 10) ÷ (3 ∗ 4) = 3

---

21. Complete.

a. 25% of 28 = __7__   b. 40% of 60 = __24__   c. 250% of 12 = __30__

22. Write each fraction as a decimal and as a percent.

a. $\frac{19}{20}$ = __0__.__95__ = __95__ %

b. $\frac{2}{3}$ = __0__.__66̄__ = __66⅔__ %

c. $\frac{12}{16}$ = __0__.__75__ = __75__ %

d. $\frac{2}{50}$ = __0__.__04__ = __4__ %

23. Insert >, <, or = to make each number sentence true.

a. $-\frac{2}{3}$ __<__ $-\frac{1}{3}$

b. $-\frac{4}{8}$ __<__ $-\frac{1}{4}$

c. −16.2 __<__ −14.6

d. −0.8 __=__ $-\frac{4}{5}$

24. Multiply and divide. Show your work.

a. __25.55__ = 7.3 ∗ 3.5

b. 228.6 / 6 = __38.1__

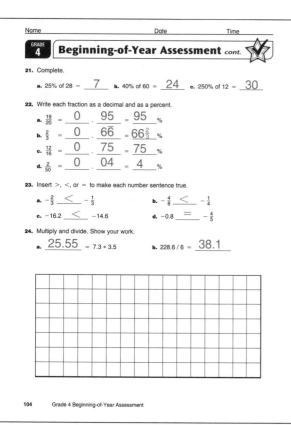

---

25. Estimate. Is the sum or difference closest to 0, 1, or 2?

a. $\frac{1}{7} + \frac{1}{6}$ __0__

b. $\frac{1}{3} + \frac{3}{4}$ __1__

c. $3\frac{3}{14} - \frac{7}{8}$ __2__

d. $\frac{9}{10} - \frac{6}{7}$ __0__

26. Use your protractor. Measure each angle below to the nearest degree.

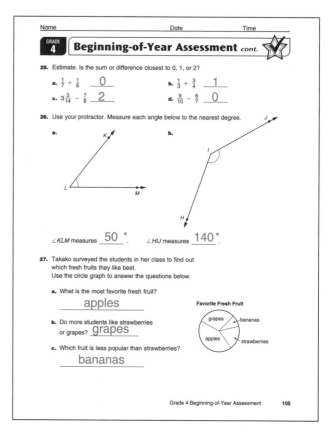

a.

K
L   M

b.

J
I
H

∠KLM measures __50__ °.

∠HIJ measures __140__ °.

27. Takako surveyed the students in her class to find out which fresh fruits they like best. Use the circle graph to answer the questions below.

a. What is the most favorite fresh fruit?

__apples__

b. Do more students like strawberries or grapes? __grapes__

c. Which fruit is less popular than strawberries?

__bananas__

Favorite Fresh Fruit

grapes — bananas
apples — strawberries

Panel 1 (page 106)

LESSON 6·11 **Mid-Year Assessment**

Part A

1. Write each number with digits.

 a. Twelve thousand, five hundred sixty-five   12,565

 b. Four million, six hundred thousand, twenty-seven   4,600,027

 c. Twelve and four-tenths   12.4

 d. Five and sixteen-hundredths   5.16

2. List the factor pairs of 32.

 1 and 32
 2 and 16
 4 and 8

3. Name the first 10 multiples of 9.

 9   18   27   36   45
 54   63   72   81   90

4. Nishi wanted to show the number 54 on her calculator. The 4-key on her calculator was broken, so this is what she did: 108 ÷ 2 =

 Find two other ways to show 54 without using the 4-key. Try to use different numbers and operations.

 a. Sample answer: 18 ⊗ 3 =

 b. Sample answer: 27 ⊕ 27 =

Complete the "What's My Rule?" tables and state the rules.

5. Rule: + 900

in	out
600	1,500
300	1,200
400	1,300
1,200	2,100
800	1,700

6. Rule: * 6

in	out
700	4,200
200	1,200
50	300
8,000	4,800
400	2,400

Panel 2 (page 107)

LESSON 6·11 **Mid-Year Assessment** *continued*

Solve. Use paper-and-pencil algorithms.

7. A gallon of skim milk costs $3.09 at the Gem supermarket and $4.19 at the 6-to-Midnight convenience store. How much more does a gallon of milk cost at the convenience store?

 $ 1.10

8. Keena bought some supplies for school. The crayons cost $1.29, the notebooks cost $2.49, and the pencils cost $0.89. How much did Keena spend in all?

 $ 4.67

9. 5,830 = 3,551 + 2,279

10. 2,653 − 1,289 = 1,364

11. 7 * 128 = 896

12. 55 = 385 / 7

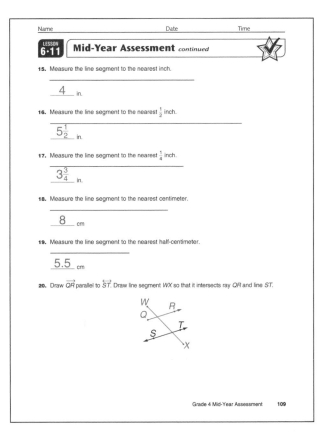

Panel 3 (page 108)

LESSON 6·11 **Mid-Year Assessment** *continued*

13. A farm stand sells apples. The farmer records how many pounds of each type of apple are sold per day. Below are the results of Monday's sales:

 18 Red Delicious   25 Gala   24 Fuji
 21 Granny Smith   17 Empire   14 Pink Lady

 Create a bar graph using the data above. Include labels and a title.

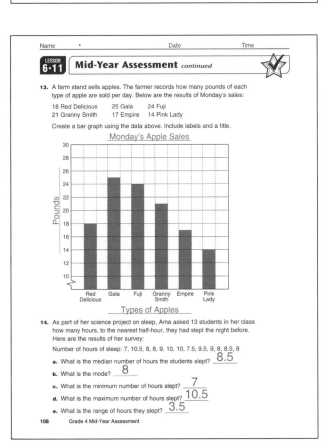

14. As part of her science project on sleep, Ama asked 13 students in her class how many hours, to the nearest half-hour, they had slept the night before. Here are the results of her survey:

 Number of hours of sleep: 7, 10.5, 8, 8, 9, 10, 10, 7.5, 9.5, 9, 8, 8.5, 8

 a. What is the median number of hours the students slept?   8.5

 b. What is the mode?   8

 c. What is the minimum number of hours slept?   7

 d. What is the maximum number of hours slept?   10.5

 e. What is the range of hours they slept?   3.5

Panel 4 (page 109)

LESSON 6·11 **Mid-Year Assessment** *continued*

15. Measure the line segment to the nearest inch.

 4 in.

16. Measure the line segment to the nearest $\frac{1}{2}$ inch.

 $5\frac{1}{2}$ in.

17. Measure the line segment to the nearest $\frac{1}{4}$ inch.

 $3\frac{3}{4}$ in.

18. Measure the line segment to the nearest centimeter.

 8 cm

19. Measure the line segment to the nearest half-centimeter.

 5.5 cm

20. Draw $\overrightarrow{QR}$ parallel to $\overleftrightarrow{ST}$. Draw line segment *WX* so that it intersects ray *QR* and line *ST*.

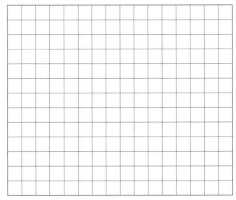

Grade 4 Assessment Answers   **195**

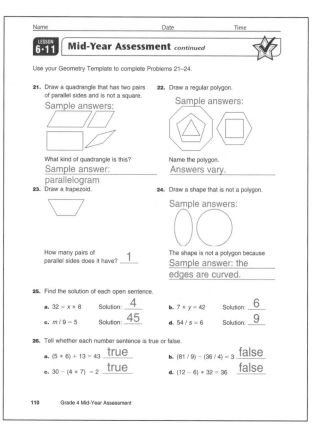

LESSON 6·11 **Mid-Year Assessment** continued

Use your Geometry Template to complete Problems 21–24.

21. Draw a quadrangle that has two pairs of parallel sides and is not a square.
Sample answers:

What kind of quadrangle is this?
Sample answer: parallelogram

23. Draw a trapezoid.

How many pairs of parallel sides does it have? __1__

22. Draw a regular polygon.
Sample answers:

Name the polygon.
Answers vary.

24. Draw a shape that is not a polygon.
Sample answers:

The shape is not a polygon because
Sample answer: the edges are curved.

25. Find the solution of each open sentence.
a. $32 = x * 8$ Solution: __4__
b. $7 * y = 42$ Solution: __6__
c. $m / 9 = 5$ Solution: __45__
d. $54 / s = 6$ Solution: __9__

26. Tell whether each number sentence is true or false.
a. $(5 * 6) + 13 = 43$ __true__
b. $(81 / 9) - (36 / 4) = 3$ __false__
c. $30 - (4 * 7) = 2$ __true__
d. $(12 - 6) * 32 = 36$ __false__

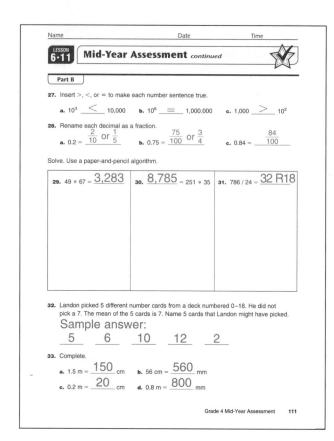

LESSON 6·11 **Mid-Year Assessment** continued

Part B

27. Insert >, <, or = to make each number sentence true.
a. 10^3 __<__ 10,000   b. 10^6 __=__ 1,000,000   c. 1,000 __>__ 10^2

28. Rename each decimal as a fraction.
a. $0.2 = \frac{2}{10}$ or $\frac{1}{5}$ b. $0.75 = \frac{75}{100}$ or $\frac{3}{4}$ c. $0.84 = \frac{84}{100}$

Solve. Use a paper-and-pencil algorithm.

29. $49 * 67 = $ __3,283__   30. $\frac{8,785}{251} = 251 * 35$ 31. $786 / 24 = $ __32 R18__

32. Landon picked 5 different number cards from a deck numbered 0–18. He did not pick a 7. The mean of the 5 cards is 7. Name 5 cards that Landon might have picked.
Sample answer:
__5__   __6__   __10__   __12__   __2__

33. Complete.
a. 1.5 m = __150__ cm   b. 56 cm = __560__ mm
c. 0.2 m = __20__ cm   d. 0.8 m = __800__ mm

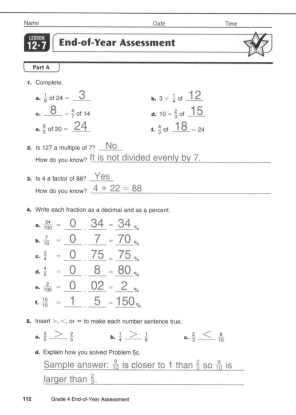

LESSON 12·7 **End-of-Year Assessment**

Part A

1. Complete.
a. $\frac{1}{8}$ of 24 = __3__   b. $3 = \frac{1}{4}$ of __12__
c. __8__ $= \frac{4}{7}$ of 14   d. $10 = \frac{2}{3}$ of __15__
e. $\frac{6}{5}$ of 20 = __24__   f. $\frac{4}{3}$ of __18__ = 24

2. Is 127 a multiple of 7? __No__
How do you know? It is not divided evenly by 7.

3. Is 4 a factor of 88? __Yes__
How do you know? $4 * 22 = 88$

4. Write each fraction as a decimal and as a percent.
a. $\frac{34}{100} = $ __0__.__34__ = __34__%
b. $\frac{7}{10} = $ __0__.__7__ = __70__%
c. $\frac{3}{4} = $ __0__.__75__ = __75__%
d. $\frac{4}{5} = $ __0__.__8__ = __80__%
e. $\frac{2}{100} = $ __0__.__02__ = __2__%
f. $\frac{15}{10} = $ __1__.__5__ = __150__%

5. Insert >, <, or = to make each number sentence true.
a. $\frac{3}{5}$ __>__ $\frac{2}{5}$ b. $\frac{1}{4}$ __>__ $\frac{1}{6}$ c. $\frac{2}{3}$ __<__ $\frac{9}{10}$

d. Explain how you solved Problem 5c.
Sample answer: $\frac{9}{10}$ is closer to 1 than $\frac{2}{3}$ so $\frac{9}{10}$ is larger than $\frac{2}{3}$.

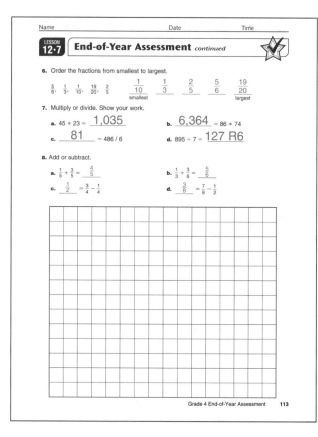

LESSON 12·7 **End-of-Year Assessment** continued

6. Order the fractions from smallest to largest.
$\frac{5}{6}$, $\frac{1}{3}$, $\frac{1}{10}$, $\frac{19}{20}$, $\frac{2}{5}$

$\frac{1}{10}$ _smallest_ $\frac{1}{3}$ $\frac{2}{5}$ $\frac{5}{6}$ $\frac{19}{20}$ _largest_

7. Multiply or divide. Show your work.
a. $45 * 23 = $ __1,035__   b. __6,364__ $= 86 * 74$
c. __81__ $= 486 / 6$ d. $895 \div 7 = $ __127 R6__

8. Add or subtract.
a. $\frac{1}{5} + \frac{3}{5} = $ __$\frac{4}{5}$__   b. $\frac{1}{3} + \frac{3}{6} = $ __$\frac{5}{6}$__
c. __$\frac{1}{2}$__ $= \frac{3}{4} - \frac{1}{4}$ d. __$\frac{3}{8}$__ $= \frac{7}{8} - \frac{1}{2}$

Page 114 (top left)

Name ___ Date ___ Time ___

LESSON 12·7 **End-of-Year Assessment** *continued*

9. The table shows the number of people who attended lacrosse games each week during the spring season. Create a line graph to show the data. Use a straightedge to connect the data points. Label each axis and include a title.

Week	Number of People
1	60
2	80
3	40
4	100
5	100
6	80
7	120
8	110

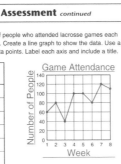

Game Attendance

10. Use the following terms to complete the statements below.

impossible
likely
unlikely
very likely

a. It is __likely__ that the spinner will land on a number less than or equal to 2.

b. It is __very likely__ that the spinner will land on a number not equal to 5.

c. It is __impossible__ that the spinner will land on a number less than $\frac{9}{10}$.

d. It is __unlikely__ that the spinner will land on 5.

114   Grade 4 End-of-Year Assessment

Page 115 (top right)

Name ___ Date ___ Time ___

LESSON 12·7 **End-of-Year Assessment** *continued*

11. Complete.

a. Color $\frac{1}{4}$ of the spinner at the right. $\frac{3}{4}$

b. What fraction of the spinner is *not* colored? $\frac{3}{4}$

c. What *percent* of the spinner is colored? __25%__

d. If you spin the spinner 100 times, about how many times would you expect it to land on the colored part? __25__ times

e. If you spin the spinner 300 times, about how many times would you expect it to land on the colored part? __75__ times

12. Use these formulas to calculate the areas of the figures below.

Rectangle	Parallelogram	Triangle
Area = base * height	Area = base * height	Area = $\frac{1}{2}$ * (base * height)

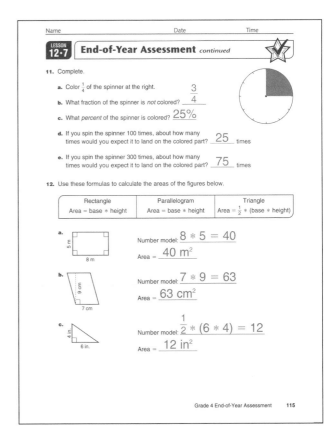

a. Number model: $8 * 5 = 40$
Area = __40 m²__

b. Number model: $7 * 9 = 63$
Area = __63 cm²__

c. Number model: $\frac{1}{2} * (6 * 4) = 12$
Area = __12 in²__

Grade 4 End-of-Year Assessment   115

Page 116 (bottom left)

Name ___ Date ___ Time ___

LESSON 12·7 **End-of-Year Assessment** *continued*

13. Calculate the volume of each rectangular prism.

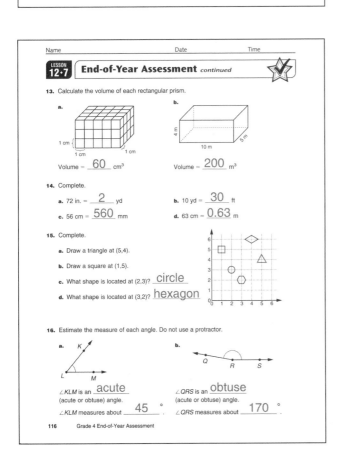

a. Volume = __60__ cm³

b. Volume = __200__ m³

14. Complete.

a. 72 in. = __2__ yd

b. 10 yd = __30__ ft

c. 56 cm = __560__ mm

d. 63 cm = __0.63__ m

15. Complete.

a. Draw a triangle at (5,4).

b. Draw a square at (1,5).

c. What shape is located at (2,3)? __circle__

d. What shape is located at (3,2)? __hexagon__

16. Estimate the measure of each angle. Do not use a protractor.

a. ∠KLM is an __acute__ (acute or obtuse) angle.
∠KLM measures about __45__°.

b. ∠QRS is an __obtuse__ (acute or obtuse) angle.
∠QRS measures about __170__°.

116   Grade 4 End-of-Year Assessment

Page 117 (bottom right)

Name ___ Date ___ Time ___

LESSON 12·7 **End-of-Year Assessment** *continued*

17. The objects below have the shapes of geometric solids. Name the solids.

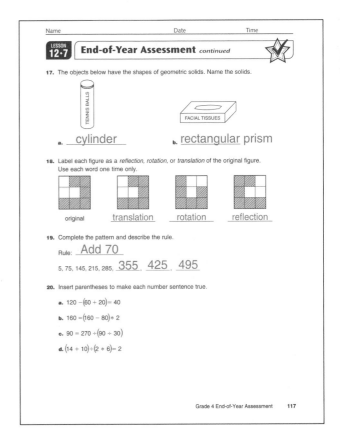

TENNIS BALLS

FACIAL TISSUES

a. __cylinder__   b. __rectangular prism__

18. Label each figure as a *reflection*, *rotation*, or *translation* of the original figure. Use each word one time only.

original   __translation__   __rotation__   __reflection__

19. Complete the pattern and describe the rule.

Rule: __Add 70__

5, 75, 145, 215, 285, __355__, __425__, __495__

20. Insert parentheses to make each number sentence true.

a. 120 − (60 + 20) = 40

b. 160 = (160 − 80) * 2

c. 90 = 270 ÷ (90 ÷ 30)

d. (14 + 10) ÷ (2 * 6) = 2

Grade 4 End-of-Year Assessment   117

Grade 4 Assessment Answers   **197**

LESSON 12·7 **End-of-Year Assessment** *continued*

Part B

21. Complete.

a. 25% of 24 = __6__   b. 30% of 50 = __15__   c. 150% of 14 = __21__

22. Write each fraction as a decimal and as a percent.

a. $\frac{17}{20}$ = __0__ . __85__ = __85__ %

b. $\frac{1}{3}$ = __0__ . __33̄__ = __33$\frac{1}{3}$__ %

c. $\frac{4}{16}$ = __0__ . __25__ = __25__ %

d. $\frac{3}{50}$ = __0__ . __06__ = __6__ %

23. Insert >, <, or = to make each number sentence true.

a. $-\frac{1}{4}$ __>__ $-\frac{3}{4}$ b. $-\frac{4}{10}$ __>__ $-\frac{4}{5}$

c. -14.6 __<__ -12.8 d. -0.6 __=__ $-\frac{3}{5}$

24. Multiply and divide. Show your work.

a. __31.05__ = 4.5 * 6.9   b. 212.4 / 9 = __23.6__

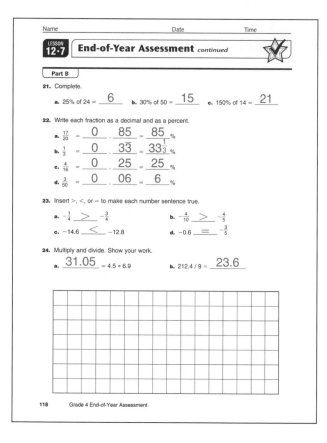

LESSON 12·7 **End-of-Year Assessment** *continued*

25. Estimate. Is the sum or difference closest to 0, 1, or 2?

a. $\frac{1}{5} + \frac{1}{8}$ __0__   b. $1\frac{2}{3} + \frac{1}{2}$ __2__

c. $2\frac{1}{12} - \frac{9}{10}$ __1__   d. $\frac{7}{8} - \frac{5}{6}$ __0__

26. Use your protractor. Measure each angle below to the nearest degree.

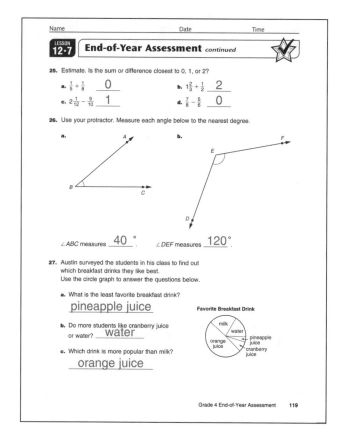

∠ABC measures __40__ °.   ∠DEF measures __120__ °.

27. Austin surveyed the students in his class to find out which breakfast drinks they like best.
Use the circle graph to answer the questions below.

a. What is the least favorite breakfast drink?
   pineapple juice

b. Do more students like cranberry juice or water? __water__

c. Which drink is more popular than milk?
   orange juice

Favorite Breakfast Drink

Page 120

Name _____ Date _____ Time _____

GRADE 5 | **Beginning-of-Year Assessment**

1. A figure is partly hidden. Which of the following might it be? (Circle all possible answers.)

rectangle
(triangle)
(trapezoid)
square

2. Add two numbers to the data set below so that
- the median of the new data set is 9,
- the maximum is 17, and
- the range is 14.

8   15   6   11   9   __3__   __17__

3. Write the following numbers in expanded notation.

a. 3,049 = __3,000 + 40 + 9__

b. 56.25 = __50 + 6 + 0.2 + 0.05__

4. A package of party favors contains 10 favors. Mr. Thomas is expecting 42 people at his party. He wants to have enough party favors for each person to have 2. How many packages of favors should he buy? __9 packages__

5. A ribbon is $8\frac{1}{4}$ inches long. If you cut off $\frac{3}{8}$ of an inch, how much is left? __$7\frac{7}{8}$__ inches

6. Sean combined $\frac{2}{3}$ cup of cheddar cheese with $\frac{1}{4}$ cup of American cheese.

Is the total cheese more or less than 1 cup? __less__

Explain. __Sample answer: It is less than a cup__
__because $\frac{2}{3} + \frac{1}{4} = \frac{11}{12}$ cup.__

120   Grade 5 Beginning-of-Year Assessment

Page 121

Name _____ Date _____ Time _____

GRADE 5 | **Beginning-of-Year Assessment**

7. Complete the table.

Standard Notation	Exponential Notation	Repeated-Factor Notation
32	2^5	2*2*2*2*2
10,000	10^4	10*10*10*10
343	7^3	7*7*7

Each square in the grid below has an area of 1 square centimeter.

8. What is the area of triangle *TOP*? __10__ cm²

9. Draw a rectangle that has an area of 14 cm². Sample answer:

10. What is the perimeter of this rectangle? __18__ cm

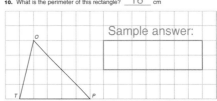
Sample answer:

11. Insert parentheses to make the number sentences true.

$(120 \div 4)*(3 + 7) = 300$ $180 = (37 - 8 + 16)*4$

12. Kelsey said that she could use just the numbers 12, 3, and 36 to write four true number sentences. Is Kelsey correct? __Yes__ Why or why not?

__12 * 3 = 36, so these three numbers form a__
__multiplication/division fact family. Kelsey can write the__
__following four number sentences with only these three__
__numbers: 12 * 3 = 36, 3 * 12 = 36, 36 / 3 = 12,__
__and 36 / 12 = 3.__

Grade 5 Beginning-of-Year Assessment   121

Page 122

Name _____ Date _____ Time _____

GRADE 5 | **Beginning-of-Year Assessment**

13. Circle the equivalent numbers.

$\left(\frac{4}{20}\right)$ 0.2   80% $\left(\frac{1}{5}\right)$ $\frac{38}{40}$ $\frac{15}{16}$ $\left(20\%\right)$

Use >, <, or =.

14. $\frac{3}{5}$ __>__ $\frac{3}{6}$ **15.** $2\frac{2}{3}$ __>__ $\frac{25}{12}$ **16.** $\frac{3}{9}$ __=__ 0.33

17. Plot the ordered pairs on the grid. Connect the points in the same order they were plotted. (1,9); (3,9); (4,9); (7,9); (9,9); (7,7); (5,7); (3,7); (2,8); (1,9)

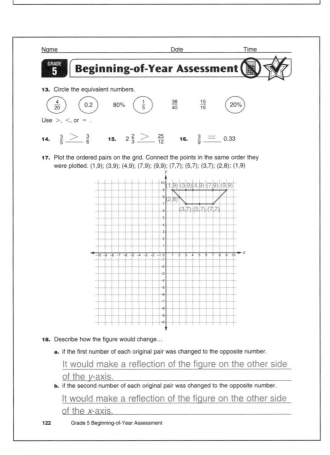

18. Describe how the figure would change…

a. if the first number of each original pair was changed to the opposite number.

__It would make a reflection of the figure on the other side__
__of the y-axis.__

b. if the second number of each original pair was changed to the opposite number.

__It would make a reflection of the figure on the other side__
__of the x-axis.__

122   Grade 5 Beginning-of-Year Assessment

Page 123

Name _____ Date _____ Time _____

GRADE 5 | **Beginning-of-Year Assessment**

19. Write the 8-digit number that has a 6 in the tens place, a 2 in the hundredths place, an 8 in the hundred-thousands place, and a 1 in all the other places.
__8 1 1 , 1 6 1 1 2__

20. What is the probability of drawing a jack of diamonds from a regular deck of 52 cards? __$\frac{1}{52}$, or about 2%__

21. What is the probability of drawing a 9 from a regular deck of 52 cards? __$\frac{4}{52}$, or $\frac{1}{13}$, or about 8%__

22. Measure the angles below.

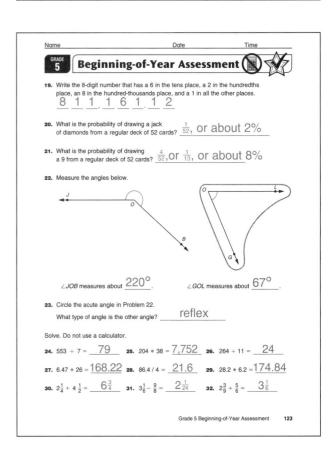

∠*JOB* measures about __220°__.   ∠*GOL* measures about __67°__.

23. Circle the acute angle in Problem 22.
What type of angle is the other angle? __reflex__

Solve. Do not use a calculator.

24. 553 ÷ 7 = __79__   **25.** 204 * 38 = __7,752__   **26.** 264 ÷ 11 = __24__

27. 6.47 * 26 = __168.22__   **28.** 86.4 / 4 = __21.6__   **29.** 28.2 * 6.2 = __174.84__

30. $2\frac{1}{4} + 4\frac{1}{2}$ = __$6\frac{3}{4}$__   **31.** $3\frac{1}{6} - \frac{9}{8}$ = __$2\frac{1}{24}$__   **32.** $2\frac{3}{9} + \frac{5}{6}$ = __$3\frac{1}{6}$__

Grade 5 Beginning-of-Year Assessment   123

GRADE 5 Beginning-of-Year Assessment

33. Mark the following points on the ruler.

A: $\frac{1}{8}$ B: $2\frac{1}{4}$ C: $1\frac{3}{16}$ D: $2\frac{13}{16}$ E: $\frac{12}{8}$

A   C E   B   D (ruler)

34. Write the prime factorization for 290. $2 * 5 * 29$

Write each fraction in its simplest form.

35. $\frac{37}{4} =$ $9\frac{1}{4}$ **36.** $5\frac{12}{32} =$ $5\frac{3}{8}$ **37.** $\frac{50}{7} =$ $7\frac{1}{7}$

38. $\frac{60}{5} =$ 12 **39.** $4\frac{12}{36} =$ $4\frac{1}{3}$ **40.** $16\frac{60}{75} =$ $16\frac{4}{5}$

41. If $\frac{5}{6}$ of a set is 20, how many are in the whole set? 24

Explain your solution strategy. I divided 20 by 5 to find $\frac{1}{6}$ of the set. Since $\frac{1}{6}$ of the set is 4, the whole set is 4 * 6, or 24.

Write >, <, or =.

42. -4 $<$ 4 **43.** -20 $<$ -15 **44.** -0.25 $>$ -0.5

45. $-5 + 5$ $=$ 0 **46.** $-3 - (-6)$ $>$ $4 + (-7)$ **47.** $15 + (-5)$ $<$ $10 + 10$

48. Circle the number sentences that are true.

$5 + (7 * 4) = 40$ $36 = 2^2 + 3 * 7$ $\boxed{30 / (2 + 8 + 5) = 2}$

$0 = (-5 + 3) * 2$ $\boxed{37 - 15 / 5 + 8 = 42}$ $\boxed{18 / 3 + 3 * 4 = 18}$

GRADE 5 Beginning-of-Year Assessment

49. Write an open number sentence. Then solve the problem.

Claudia was cleaning her collection of seashells. She had already cleaned 28 of them. If that was $\frac{7}{8}$ of them, how many did she have left to clean?

Open sentence: $28 \div 7 =$

Answer: 4 seashells

Explain: If she had finished $\frac{7}{8}$, she still had $\frac{1}{8}$ left to clean. Divide 28 by 7 to find how many are in one-eighth.

50. Complete the table. Then graph the data in the table.

Rule: Number of miles = days * 36 miles

Time (days)	Number of miles
1	36
4	144
3	108
2	72
3.5	126

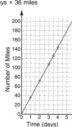

51. What is the volume of the prism to the right? 60 in^3 (unit)

52. A cylindrical can has a base with an area of 16.4 square centimeters. It has a height of 10 centimeters. What is its volume? 164 cm^3 (unit)

Volume of a prism: $V = B * h$

Volume of a cylinder: $V = B * h$

GRADE 5 Beginning-of-Year Assessment

Find the missing number.

53. $\frac{1}{3} = \frac{17}{x}$ $x =$ 51 **54.** $\frac{10}{16} = \frac{s}{8}$ $s =$ 5

55. $\frac{n}{200} = \frac{2}{5}$ $n =$ 80 **56.** $\frac{45}{m} = \frac{5}{8}$ $m =$ 72

Complete the table.

	Exponential Notation	Standard Notation	Number-and-Word Notation
57.	$2 * 10^4$	20,000	20 thousand
58.	$9 * 10^6$	9,000,000	9 million
59.	$3.7 * 10^8$	370,000,000	3.7 hundred-million
60.	$4.6 * 10^9$	4,600,000,000	4.6 billion

61. Shorts sell for $15.00 each. With a shopper's card, the price is discounted 20%. There is an additional 10% off the discounted total cost if you buy two or more pairs. What is the discounted cost of 3 pairs of shorts? Show your work on the back of this page.

Discounted cost: $32.40

Find the greatest common factor for each pair of numbers below.

62. 32 and 80 16   **63.** 80 and 20 20

Find the least common multiple for each pair of numbers below.

64. 5 and 10 10   **65.** 4 and 10 20

GRADE 5 Beginning-of-Year Assessment *cont.*

66. Circle the figure below that has the greatest volume.

cone   square pyramid   cube

Volume of a cone: $V = \frac{1}{3} * (B * h)$

Volume of a pyramid: $V = \frac{1}{3} * (B * h)$

Volume of a prism: $V = B * h$

Explain: The pyramid's volume is one-third the volume of the cube. The cone's volume is smaller than the cube because the height is the same, but the area of its base is smaller and you have to divide by 3.

Solve. Write your answers in simplest form.

67. a. $\frac{6}{7} * \frac{12}{14} =$ $\frac{36}{49}$ **b.** $10\frac{3}{4} * \frac{4}{6} =$ $7\frac{1}{6}$ **c.** $4\frac{2}{7} * 3\frac{3}{5} =$ $15\frac{3}{7}$

68. a. $\frac{5}{6} \div \frac{1}{12} =$ 10 **b.** $11\frac{2}{3} \div 9\frac{5}{6} =$ $1\frac{11}{59}$ **c.** $\frac{1}{4} \div \frac{7}{8} =$ $\frac{2}{7}$

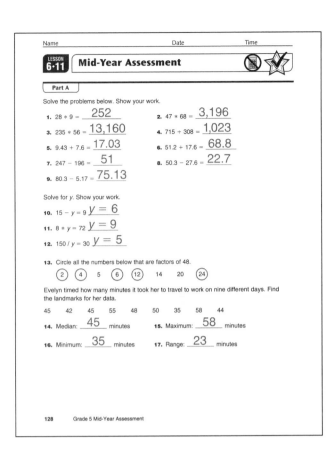

Name   Date   Time

LESSON 6·11   Mid-Year Assessment

Part A

Solve the problems below. Show your work.

1. 28 * 9 = __252__   2. 47 * 68 = __3,196__

3. 235 * 56 = __13,160__   4. 715 + 308 = __1,023__

5. 9.43 + 7.6 = __17.03__   6. 51.2 + 17.6 = __68.8__

7. 247 − 196 = __51__   8. 50.3 − 27.6 = __22.7__

9. 80.3 − 5.17 = __75.13__

Solve for y. Show your work.

10. 15 − y = 9 $y = 6$

11. 8 * y = 72 $y = 9$

12. 150 / y = 30 $y = 5$

13. Circle all the numbers below that are factors of 48.

(2) (4) 5 (6) (12) 14 20 (24)

Evelyn timed how many minutes it took her to travel to work on nine different days. Find the landmarks for her data.

45   42   45   55   48   50   35   58   44

14. Median: __45__ minutes   15. Maximum: __58__ minutes

16. Minimum: __35__ minutes   17. Range: __23__ minutes

128   Grade 5 Mid-Year Assessment

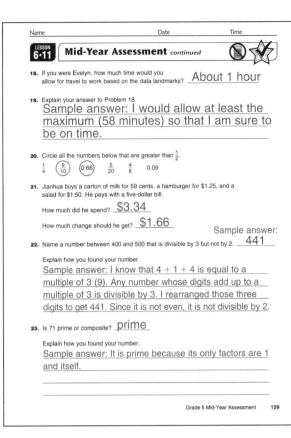

Name   Date   Time

LESSON 6·11   Mid-Year Assessment *continued*

18. If you were Evelyn, how much time would you allow for travel to work based on the data landmarks?   __About 1 hour__

19. Explain your answer to Problem 18.
Sample answer: I would allow at least the maximum (58 minutes) so that I am sure to be on time.

20. Circle all the numbers below that are greater than $\frac{1}{2}$.

$\frac{1}{4}$ $(\frac{9}{10})$ (0.66) $\frac{5}{20}$ $\frac{4}{8}$ 0.09

21. Jianhua buys a carton of milk for 59 cents, a hamburger for $1.25, and a salad for $1.50. He pays with a five-dollar bill.

How much did he spend?   __$3.34__

How much change should he get?   __$1.66__

22. Name a number between 400 and 500 that is divisible by 3 but not by 2.   Sample answer: __441__

Explain how you found your number.
Sample answer: I know that 4 + 1 + 4 is equal to a multiple of 3 (9). Any number whose digits add up to a multiple of 3 is divisible by 3. I rearranged those three digits to get 441. Since it is not even, it is not divisible by 2.

23. Is 71 prime or composite?   __prime__

Explain how you found your number.
Sample answer: It is prime because its only factors are 1 and itself.

Grade 5 Mid-Year Assessment   129

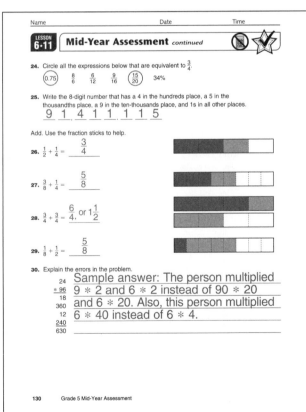

Name   Date   Time

LESSON 6·11   Mid-Year Assessment *continued*

24. Circle all the expressions below that are equivalent to $\frac{3}{4}$.

(0.75) $\frac{8}{6}$ $\frac{6}{12}$ $\frac{9}{16}$ $(\frac{15}{20})$ 34%

25. Write the 8-digit number that has a 4 in the hundreds place, a 5 in the thousandths place, a 9 in the ten-thousands place, and 1s in all other places.
__9 1 4 1 1 1 1 5__

Add. Use the fraction sticks to help.

26. $\frac{1}{2} + \frac{1}{4} = $ __$\frac{3}{4}$__

27. $\frac{3}{8} + \frac{1}{4} = $ __$\frac{5}{8}$__

28. $\frac{3}{4} + \frac{3}{4} = $ __$\frac{6}{4}$, or $1\frac{1}{2}$__

29. $\frac{1}{8} + \frac{1}{2} = $ __$\frac{5}{8}$__

30. Explain the errors in the problem.

```
   24
 * 96
   18
  360
   12
  240
  630
```
Sample answer: The person multiplied 9 * 2 and 6 * 2 instead of 90 * 20 and 6 * 20. Also, this person multiplied 6 * 40 instead of 6 * 4.

130   Grade 5 Mid-Year Assessment

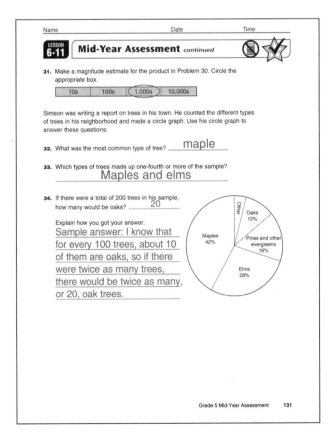

Name   Date   Time

LESSON 6·11   Mid-Year Assessment *continued*

31. Make a magnitude estimate for the product in Problem 30. Circle the appropriate box.

10s   100s   (1,000s)   10,000s

Simeon was writing a report on trees in his town. He counted the different types of trees in his neighborhood and made a circle graph. Use his circle graph to answer these questions:

32. What was the most common type of tree?   __maple__

33. Which types of trees made up one-fourth or more of the sample?
__Maples and elms__

34. If there were a total of 200 trees in his sample, how many would be oaks?   __20__

Explain how you got your answer.
Sample answer: I know that for every 100 trees, about 10 of them are oaks, so if there were twice as many trees, there would be twice as many, or 20, oak trees.

Grade 5 Mid-Year Assessment   131

LESSON 6·11 **Mid-Year Assessment** *continued*

Part B

35. Laquita wrote 2 * 2 * 3 * 5 for the prime factorization of 48. Explain why you agree or disagree with her answer.
I disagree. The prime factorization for 48 is 2 * 2 * 2 * 2 * 3.

36. Draw and label a rectangle that has a base of 6.5 cm and a height of 4 cm. Use your ruler or any other tool that you wish.

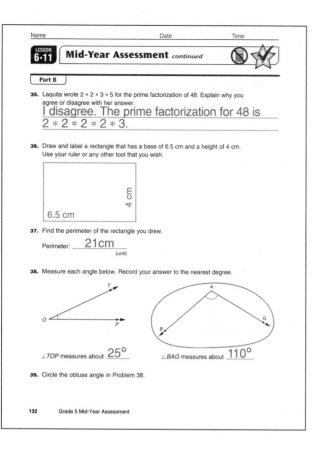

6.5 cm   4 cm

37. Find the perimeter of the rectangle you drew.
Perimeter: 21cm (unit)

38. Measure each angle below. Record your answer to the nearest degree.

∠TOP measures about 25°   ∠BAG measures about 110°

39. Circle the obtuse angle in Problem 38.

LESSON 6·11 **Mid-Year Assessment** *continued*

40. Plot the following points on the grid to the right. Connect the points.
(2,1); (3,3); (5,1); (6,3)

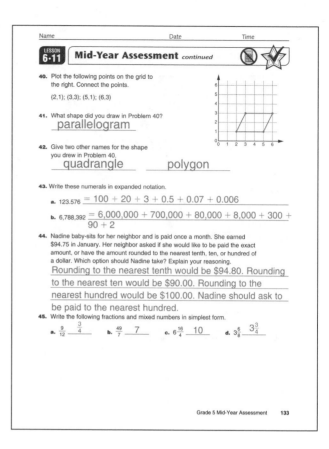

41. What shape did you draw in Problem 40?
parallelogram

42. Give two other names for the shape you drew in Problem 40.
quadrangle   polygon

43. Write these numerals in expanded notation.
a. 123.576 = 100 + 20 + 3 + 0.5 + 0.07 + 0.006
b. 6,788,392 = 6,000,000 + 700,000 + 80,000 + 8,000 + 300 + 90 + 2

44. Nadine baby-sits for her neighbor and is paid once a month. She earned $94.75 in January. Her neighbor asked if she would like to be paid the exact amount, or have the amount rounded to the nearest tenth, ten, or hundred of a dollar. Which option should Nadine take? Explain your reasoning.
Rounding to the nearest tenth would be $94.80. Rounding to the nearest ten would be $90.00. Rounding to the nearest hundred would be $100.00. Nadine should ask to be paid to the nearest hundred.

45. Write the following fractions and mixed numbers in simplest form.
a. $\frac{9}{12}$ $\frac{3}{4}$ b. $\frac{49}{7}$ 7   c. $6\frac{16}{4}$ 10   d. $3\frac{6}{8}$ $3\frac{3}{4}$

LESSON 12·9 **End-of-Year Assessment**

Part A

1. A figure is partly hidden. Which of the following might it be? (Circle all possible answers.)
(rectangle)
triangle
(trapezoid)
square

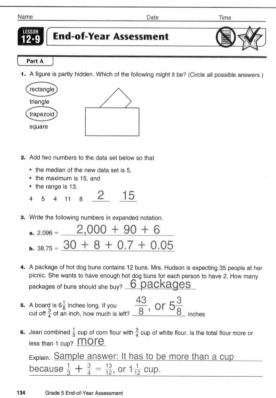

2. Add two numbers to the data set below so that
   • the median of the new data set is 5,
   • the maximum is 15, and
   • the range is 13.
   4 5 4 11 8   2   15

3. Write the following numbers in expanded notation.
a. 2,096 = 2,000 + 90 + 6
b. 38.75 = 30 + 8 + 0.7 + 0.05

4. A package of hot dog buns contains 12 buns. Mrs. Hudson is expecting 35 people at her picnic. She wants to have enough hot dog buns for each person to have 2. How many packages of buns should she buy? 6 packages

5. A board is $6\frac{1}{8}$ inches long. If you cut off $\frac{3}{4}$ of an inch, how much is left? $\frac{43}{8}$, or $5\frac{3}{8}$ inches

6. Jean combined $\frac{1}{3}$ cup of corn flour with $\frac{3}{4}$ cup of white flour. Is the total flour more or less than 1 cup? more
Explain. Sample answer: It has to be more than a cup because $\frac{1}{3} + \frac{3}{4} = \frac{13}{12}$, or $1\frac{1}{12}$ cup.

LESSON 12·9 **End-of-Year Assessment** *continued*

7. Complete the table.

Standard Notation	Exponential Notation	Repeated-Factor Notation
729	3^6	3*3*3*3*3*3
1,000	10^3	10*10*10
729	9^3	9*9*9

Each square in the grid below has an area of 1 square centimeter.

8. What is the area of triangle *END*? 10 cm²

9. Draw a rectangle that has an area of 12 cm².

10. What is the perimeter of this rectangle? Sample answer: 16 cm

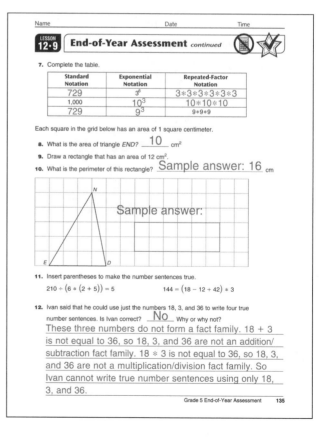

Sample answer:

11. Insert parentheses to make the number sentences true.
210 ÷ (6 * (2 + 5)) = 5   144 = (18 − 12 + 42) * 3

12. Ivan said that he could use just the numbers 18, 3, and 36 to write four true number sentences. Is Ivan correct? No Why or why not?
These three numbers do not form a fact family. 18 + 3 is not equal to 36, so 18, 3, and 36 are not an addition/subtraction fact family. 18 * 3 is not equal to 36, so 18, 3, and 36 are not a multiplication/division fact family. So Ivan cannot write true number sentences using only 18, 3, and 36.

LESSON 12·9   **End-of-Year Assessment** *continued*

13. Circle the equivalent numbers.

$\boxed{\frac{19}{20}}$ $\boxed{0.95}$ 19% $\frac{1}{5}$ $\boxed{\frac{38}{40}}$ $\frac{15}{16}$ $\boxed{95\%}$

Use >, <, or .

14. $\frac{3}{8}$ $<$ $\frac{3}{7}$ **15.** $3\frac{2}{3}$ $>$ $\frac{24}{10}$ **16.** $\frac{5}{15}$ $<$ 0.66

17. Plot the ordered pairs on the grid. Connect the points in the same order they were plotted. (1,1); (4,1); (6,1); (9,1); (8,3); (7,5); (5,5); (3,5); (2,3);

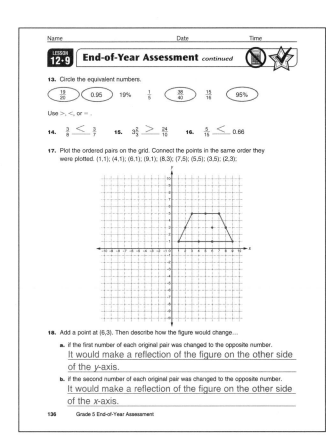

18. Add a point at (6,3). Then describe how the figure would change…

  a. if the first number of each original pair was changed to the opposite number.

  It would make a reflection of the figure on the other side of the *y*-axis.

  b. if the second number of each original pair was changed to the opposite number.

  It would make a reflection of the figure on the other side of the *x*-axis.

LESSON 12·9   **End-of-Year Assessment** *continued*

19. Write the 8-digit number that has a 5 in the tens place, a 3 in the hundredths place, a 4 in the hundred-thousands place, and 8 in all the other places.

  4 8 8 . 8 5 8 8 3

20. What is the probability of drawing a king of hearts from a regular deck of 52 cards? $\frac{1}{52}$, or about 2%

21. What is the probability of drawing a 5 from a regular deck of 52 cards? $\frac{4}{52}$, or $\frac{1}{13}$ about 8%

22. Measure the angles below.

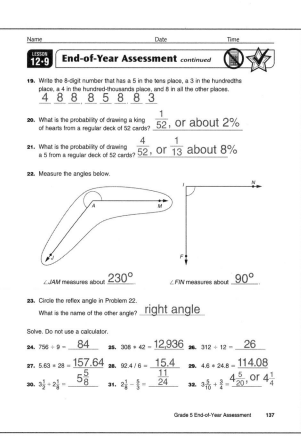

∠*JAM* measures about 230°   ∠*FIN* measures about 90°.

23. Circle the reflex angle in Problem 22.

What is the name of the other angle?   right angle

Solve. Do not use a calculator.

24. $756 \div 9 =$ 84   **25.** $308 * 42 =$ 12,936   **26.** $312 \div 12 =$ 26

27. $5.63 * 28 =$ 157.64   **28.** $92.4 / 6 =$ 15.4   **29.** $4.6 * 24.8 =$ 114.08

30. $3\frac{1}{2} + 2\frac{1}{8} =$ $5\frac{5}{8}$ **31.** $2\frac{1}{8} - \frac{5}{3} =$ $\frac{11}{24}$ **32.** $3\frac{5}{10} + \frac{3}{4} =$ $4\frac{5}{20}$, or $4\frac{1}{4}$

LESSON 12·9   **End-of-Year Assessment** *continued*

33. Mark the following points on the ruler.

A: $\frac{7}{8}$ B: $\frac{3}{4}$ C: $1\frac{5}{16}$ D: $2\frac{11}{16}$ E: $\frac{5}{10}$

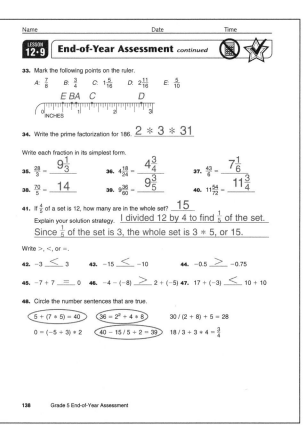

34. Write the prime factorization for 186.   2 * 3 * 31

Write each fraction in its simplest form.

35. $\frac{28}{3} =$ $9\frac{1}{3}$ **36.** $4\frac{18}{24} =$ $4\frac{3}{4}$ **37.** $\frac{43}{6} =$ $7\frac{1}{6}$

38. $\frac{70}{5} =$ 14   **39.** $9\frac{36}{60} =$ $9\frac{3}{5}$ **40.** $11\frac{54}{72} =$ $11\frac{3}{4}$

41. If $\frac{4}{5}$ of a set is 12, how many are in the whole set?   15

Explain your solution strategy. I divided 12 by 4 to find $\frac{1}{5}$ of the set.

Since $\frac{1}{5}$ of the set is 3, the whole set is 3 * 5, or 15.

Write >, <, or =.

42. -3 $<$ 3   **43.** -15 $<$ -10 **44.** -0.5 $>$ -0.75

45. $-7 + 7$ $=$ 0   **46.** $-4 - (-8)$ $>$ $2 + (-5)$ **47.** $17 + (-3)$ $<$ $10 + 10$

48. Circle the number sentences that are true.

$\boxed{5 + (7 * 5) = 40}$ $\boxed{36 = 2^2 + 4 * 8}$ $30 / (2 + 8) + 5 = 28$

$0 = (-5 + 3) * 2$ $\boxed{40 - 15 / 5 + 2 = 39}$ $18 / 3 + 3 * 4 = \frac{3}{4}$

LESSON 12·9   **End-of-Year Assessment** *continued*

49. Write an open number sentence. Then solve the problem.

Maureen was cleaning her collection of toy elephants. She had already cleaned 24 of them. If that was $\frac{6}{7}$ of them, how many did she have left to clean?

Open sentence: $24 \div 6 =$

Answer: 4 toy elephants

Explain: If she had finished $\frac{6}{7}$, she still had $\frac{1}{7}$ left to clean.

Divide 24 by 6 to find how many are in one-seventh.

50. Complete the table. Then graph the data in the table.

Rule: Number of words = minutes * 46 words

Time (min)	Number of words
1	46
4	184
3	138
2	92
2.5	115

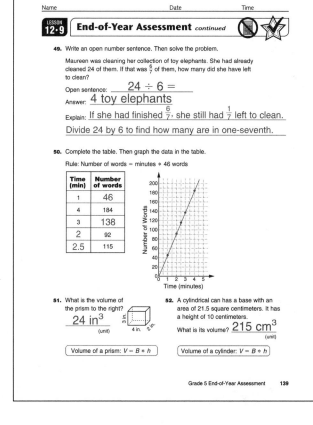

51. What is the volume of the prism to the right?

24 in³
(unit)

Volume of a prism: $V = B * h$

52. A cylindrical can has a base with an area of 21.5 square centimeters. It has a height of 10 centimeters.

What is its volume?   215 cm³
(unit)

Volume of a cylinder: $V = B * h$

LESSON 12·9 End-of-Year Assessment *continued*

Part B

Find the missing number.

53. $\frac{1}{5} = \frac{19}{x}$ $x = $ __95__

54. $\frac{8}{20} = \frac{s}{10}$ $s = $ __4__

55. $\frac{n}{120} = \frac{3}{4}$ $n = $ __90__

56. $\frac{36}{m} = \frac{4}{7}$ $m = $ __63__

Complete the table.

	Exponential Notation	Standard Notation	Number-and-Word Notation
57.	$2 * 10^3$	2,000	2 thousand
58.	$8 * 10^6$	8,000,000	8 million
59.	$4.6 * 10^8$	460,000,000	4.6 hundred-million
60.	$2.3 * 10^9$	2,300,000,000	2.3 billion

61. Pairs of cargo pants sell for $18.00 each. With a shopper's card, the price is discounted 25%. There is an additional 10% off the total cost if you buy two or more pairs. What is the discounted cost of 3 pairs of cargo pants? Show your work on the back of this page.

Discounted cost: __$36.45__

Find the greatest common factor for each pair of numbers below.

62. 24 and 60 __12__

63. 100 and 25 __25__

Find the least common multiple for each pair of numbers below.

64. 4 and 8 __8__

65. 6 and 9 __18__

LESSON 12·9 End-of-Year Assessment *continued*

66. Circle the figure below that has the greatest volume.

cube   square pyramid   cone

Volume of a prism: $V = B * h$

Volume of a pyramid: $V = \frac{1}{3} * (B * h)$

Volume of a cone: $V = \frac{1}{3} * (B * h)$

Explain. __The pyramid's volume is one-third the volume of the cube. The cone's volume is smaller than the cube because the height is the same, but the area of its base is smaller and you have to divide by 3.__

Solve. Write your answers in simplest form.

67. a. $\frac{7}{8} * \frac{14}{16} = $ __$\frac{49}{64}$__

b. $12\frac{3}{5} * \frac{5}{6} = $ __$10\frac{1}{2}$__

c. $4\frac{2}{7} * 3\frac{1}{6} = $ __$13\frac{4}{7}$__

68. a. $\frac{3}{8} \div \frac{2}{16} = $ __3__

b. $17\frac{3}{5} \div 2\frac{12}{25} = $ __$7\frac{3}{31}$__

c. $\frac{1}{2} \div \frac{5}{6} = $ __$\frac{3}{5}$__

Page 142

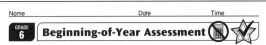

GRADE 6 Beginning-of-Year Assessment

1. Compare using >, <, or =.

a. 7 hundredths $=$ 0.07

b. 6,300,000 $>$ 6.1 million

c. $6.2 * 10^{-2}$ $>$ $7 * 10^{-3}$

d. 2^4 $<$ 24

e. 0.80 $<$ $\frac{35}{40}$

f. 0.02 $<$ 20%

2. Divide. Write your answers in simplest form.

a. $\frac{1}{4} \div 4 = \frac{1}{16}$

b. $3\frac{4}{7} \div \frac{1}{2} = 7\frac{1}{7}$

c. $6\frac{1}{5} \div 2\frac{3}{8} = 2\frac{58}{95}$

3. Use order of operations to evaluate each expression.

a. $12 \div 3 + 2 * 8 = 20$

b. $7 + 4 * 6 \div 2 - (-6) = 25$

4. Estimate each quotient. Sample estimates:

a. $39.75 \div 0.5$ Estimate 80

b. $50 \div 1.4$ Estimate 35

5. Complete the table for the given rule. Then plot the points and connect them to make a line graph.

Rule: $y = 3x + 2$

x	y
-2	-4
-1	-1
0	2
1	5
2	8

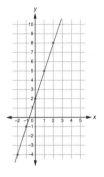

Page 143

GRADE 6 Beginning-of-Year Assessment

6. Solve.

a. $-36.7 + (-12.3) = -49.0$

b. $-\frac{9}{10} + \frac{14}{15} = \frac{1}{30}$

c. $-7 = \frac{49}{-7}$

d. $120 = -60 \div (-0.5)$

7. Is each number sentence true or false?

a. $-15 * (6 - 8) < 20$ false

b. $10 * (3 \div (-3)) \geq -3 \div \frac{7}{8}$ false

c. $(-2)^3 > (-2)^2$ true

d. $(8 * 45) + 20 = 8 * (45 + 20)$ false

Solve each equation. Show your work.

8. $2d + 8 = 24$

9. $2p + 3 + 4p = 15$

$d = 8$

$p = 2$

10. $\frac{4}{9}k + 9 = \frac{7}{9}k - 18$

11. $12r - 52 = 20 - 6r$

$k = 81$

$r = 4$

Page 144

GRADE 6 Beginning-of-Year Assessment

12. Graph the solution set for each inequality.

a. $m \geq 1 - 2$

$-5 \quad -4 \quad -3 \quad -2 \quad -1 \quad 0 \quad 1 \quad 2 \quad 3 \quad 4 \quad 5$

b. $n < -2$

$-5 \quad -4 \quad -3 \quad -2 \quad -1 \quad 0 \quad 1 \quad 2 \quad 3 \quad 4 \quad 5$

13. Tyree flips a coin two times.

a. Make an organized list or a tree diagram to display all possible outcomes.

Flip 1 | Flip 2
H | H
H | T
T | H
T | T

F1:
F2: H T H T

b. What is the probability Tyree will get 2 HEADS? Express this probability as a percent.   25%

14. Marki rolled a fair die 4 times and recorded the result of each roll in the table at the right.

roll	1st	2nd	3rd	4th
number rolled	3	2	1	2

a. What is the probability that the die will land on 2 when Marki rolls again? Express the probability as a fraction. $\frac{1}{6}$

b. About how many times would you expect Marki to get a 3 if she rolls the same fair die 468 times?   78 times

Page 145

GRADE 6 Beginning-of-Year Assessment

Solve each problem using any method.

15. Model airplane hobbyists can collect airplanes and equipment that are precise replicas of actual planes. The toy planes look exactly like the real planes they represent, only smaller.

There are four popular scales that appear in the table at the right.

Scale Name	Scale (inches) Model: Actual
A	$\frac{1}{48}$
B	$\frac{1}{150}$
C	$\frac{1}{200}$
D	$\frac{1}{500}$

a. An Air National Guard F-16 is 48 ft long. What is the length in inches of a model F-16 plane built on the A scale?   12 in.

b. A B-scale cargo transporter is 8 inches long. How long is the actual plane?   100 ft

c. A commercial 727 passenger plane is $162\frac{1}{2}$ ft long. A model is 9.75 in. long. In which scale was the model built?   C scale

16. A 10-oz can of *Math-O's* costs $3.29. A 14-oz can costs $4.34. Which can is the better buy?

a. The 14-oz can of *Math-O's* is the better buy.

b. Explain how you determined which can is the better buy.

Sample answer: I divided $4.34 by 14 ounces to get $0.31 per ounce. Because $3.29 is very close to $3.30, I estimated before dividing: $3.30 ÷ 10 is $0.33. Based on my estimate, I figured out that the 14-ounce can costs less per ounce.

17. You have 36 coins. Four out of every 9 are HEADS up. How many coins are HEADS up?   16 coins are HEADS up.

Panel 1 (page 146)

Name ___ Date ___ Time ___

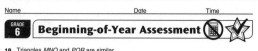

Beginning-of-Year Assessment

18. Triangles *MNO* and *PQR* are similar.

   a. Measure the sides of each triangle to the nearest millimeter. Write the measurements next to the sides.

 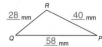

O: 14 mm, 20 mm; N — M: 29 mm

R: 28 mm, 40 mm; Q — P: 58 mm

   b. What is the size-change ratio between the two triangles? **1:2**

19. Lines *p* and *q* are parallel and intersect the *x*- and *y*-axes to form similar right triangles.

   a. What are the coordinates of point *G*?

   (**0** , **8**)

   b. Find the area of triangle *DEF*.

   Area = **6** units²

   c. Use the Pythagorean theorem to find the length of $\overline{DF}$.

   Pythagorean theorem $a^2 + b^2 = c^2$

   $\overline{DF}$ = **5** units

   d. Explain how you can use the dimensions of triangle *DEF* to find the perimeter of triangle *GER*.

   Sample answer: Because triangles *DEF* and *GER* are similar, I used a proportion to find the length of $\overline{GR}$; $\frac{6}{3} = \frac{x}{5}$; $x = 10$. $10 + 6 + 8 = 24$. The perimeter is 24 units.

Panel 2 (page 147)

Name ___ Date ___ Time ___

Beginning-of-Year Assessment

20. Write each number as a percent.

   a. 0.4 **40%**   **b.** 0.035 **3.5%**   **c.** 1.2 **120%**   **d.** 0.07 **7%**

21. Complete the table. Write each fraction in simplest form.

	Fraction	Decimal	Percent
a.	$\frac{4}{5}$	0.8	80%
b.	$\frac{13}{50}$	0.26	26%
c.	$\frac{2}{25}$	0.08	8%
d.	$\frac{1}{500}$	0.002	0.2%

Solve Problems 22–26 using any method. Show your work. **Sample work shown.**

22. Find 48% of 50.

   $0.48 * 50$

   48% of 50 is **24**.

23. What percent of 50 is 41?

   $50x = 41$

   $x = \frac{41}{50}$

   41 is **82** % of 50.

24. 80 is 20% of what number?

   $0.2x = 80$

   80 is 20% of **400**.

25. Find 130% of 60.

   $1.3 * 60$

   130% of 60 is **78**.

26. Software for a personal computer that regularly sells for $80 is on sale for 15% off. Find the sale price.

   Sale price **$68**

Panel 3 (page 148)

Name ___ Date ___ Time ___

Beginning-of-Year Assessment *cont.*

For Problems 27–30, write an equation to solve for *x*. Find any missing dimensions. You may use a calculator.

Formulas

Areas

Rectangle $b * h$
Circle πr^2

Volume

Rectangular prism $B * h$
Cylinder $B * h$

27. Regular pentagon

   $3x + 3$

   Perimeter: 75 units

   a. Equation $5(3x + 3) = 75$ **b.** x = **4**   **c.** side = **15** units

28.

   8 ; $3x + 8$; Area: 280 units²

   a. Equation $8(3x + 8) = 280$ **b.** x = **9**   **c.** base = **35** units

29.

   x ; 4 ; 10 ; Volume: 200 units³

   a. Equation $4 * 10 * x = 200$

   b. x = **5** units

30.

   12 ; x ; Volume: 792 units³

   Use $\pi = \frac{22}{7}$

   a. Equation $(\frac{22}{7})(6^2)(x) = 792$

   b. x = **7** units

Panel 4 (page 149)

Name ___ Date ___ Time ___

Beginning-of-Year Assessment

31. Find the measure of each angle without using a protractor. Lines *m* and *n* are parallel.

   a. m∠1 = **80°**   **b.** m∠2 = **60°**

   c. m∠3 = **40°**   **d.** m∠4 = **80°**

   e. m∠5 = **100°**   **f.** m∠6 = **90°**

Use triangle *ABC* with vertices at (6, 0); (9, 4); and (3,4) to complete Problem 32.

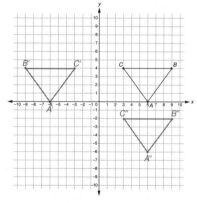

32. Draw and label the image of triangle *ABC* after

   a. a reflection over the *y*-axis. A'(**−6**, **0**); B'(**−9**, **4**); C'(**−3**, **4**)

   b. a translation 6 units down. A"(**6**, **−6**); B"(**9**, **−2**); C"(**3**, **−2**)

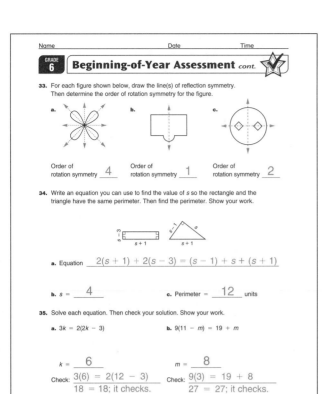

Name _____ Date _____ Time _____

GRADE 6 **Beginning-of-Year Assessment** *cont.*

33. For each figure shown below, draw the line(s) of reflection symmetry. Then determine the order of rotation symmetry for the figure.

a.   b.   c.

Order of rotation symmetry ___4___   Order of rotation symmetry ___1___   Order of rotation symmetry ___2___

34. Write an equation you can use to find the value of s so the rectangle and the triangle have the same perimeter. Then find the perimeter. Show your work.

a. Equation ___$2(s + 1) + 2(s - 3) = (s - 1) + s + (s + 1)$___

b. $s =$ ___4___   c. Perimeter = ___12___ units

35. Solve each equation. Then check your solution. Show your work.

a. $3k = 2(2k - 3)$ b. $9(11 - m) = 19 + m$

$k =$ ___6___ $m =$ ___8___

Check: $\dfrac{3(6) = 2(12 - 3)}{18 = 18;\text{ it checks.}}$ Check: $\dfrac{9(3) = 19 + 8}{27 = 27;\text{ it checks.}}$

150   Grade 6 Beginning-of-Year Assessment

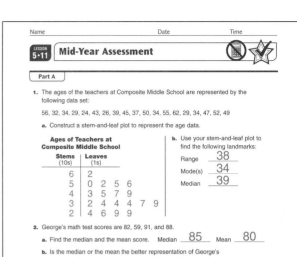

Name _____ Date _____ Time _____

LESSON 5·11 **Mid-Year Assessment**

Part A

1. The ages of the teachers at Composite Middle School are represented by the following data set:

56, 32, 34, 29, 24, 43, 26, 39, 45, 37, 50, 34, 55, 62, 29, 34, 47, 52, 49

a. Construct a stem-and-leaf plot to represent the age data.

Ages of Teachers at Composite Middle School

Stems (10s)	Leaves (1s)
6	2
5	0 2 5 6
4	3 5 7 9
3	2 4 4 4 7 9
2	4 6 9 9

b. Use your stem-and-leaf plot to find the following landmarks:

Range ___38___

Mode(s) ___34___

Median ___39___

2. George's math test scores are 82, 59, 91, and 88.

a. Find the median and the mean score. Median ___85___ Mean ___80___

b. Is the median or the mean the better representation of George's overall performance, or are they about the same? Explain your reasoning.

Sample answer: Because 4 test scores are at or above 82, the median score is a better indicator of George's overall performance.

c. Suppose George needs a mean score of 83 to earn a B in his math class and there is only one test left to take. What is the least score George can receive on this last test to get a B for the class?

___95___ Explain how you got your answer. Sample answer: five test scores will determine his average. Because $\dfrac{x + 82 + 59 + 91 + 88}{5} = 83$, $x = 95$.

Grade 6 Mid-Year Assessment   151

Name _____ Date _____ Time _____

LESSON 5·11 **Mid-Year Assessment** *continued*

3. A clothing designer surveyed adult women and men on the color of pants they preferred to wear for formal occasions. The stacked bar graph below displays the results of that survey.

a. How many men preferred blue pants?

___600___

Pant Color Preferences

(bar graph: Number of People vs Pant Color — Black, Blue, Gray, Khaki; ■ Men, □ Women)

b. Which pant color did the majority of men prefer?

___khaki___

c. About what fraction of people who preferred gray pants were women?

About ___$\frac{3}{4}$___

4. The Mouawad Splendour diamond sold for 12.76 million dollars in 1990. Write 12.76 million in

a. standard notation. ___12,760,000___

b. scientific notation. ___$1.276 * 10^7$___

5. The moon orbits at an average distance from Earth of about 384,400 kilometers. Write 384,400 in

a. number-and-word notation. ___384.4 thousand___

b. expanded notation. ($\underline{3} * 10^5$) + ($\underline{8} * 10^4$) + ($\underline{4} * 10^3$) + ($\underline{4} * 10^2$)

6. An angstrom (Å) is a unit of length. It is equivalent to 0.0000001 millimeter. Write 0.0000001 as a power of 10. ___$1 * 10^{-7}$___

152   Grade 6 Mid-Year Assessment

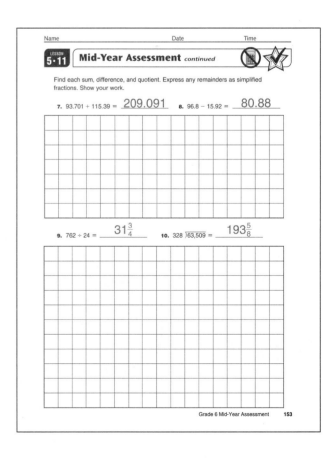

Name _____ Date _____ Time _____

LESSON 5·11 **Mid-Year Assessment** *continued*

Find each sum, difference, and quotient. Express any remainders as simplified fractions. Show your work.

7. $93.701 + 115.39 =$ ___209.091___   **8.** $96.8 - 15.92 =$ ___80.88___

9. $762 \div 24 =$ ___$31\frac{3}{4}$___   **10.** $328\overline{)63,509}$ ___$193\frac{5}{8}$___

Grade 6 Mid-Year Assessment   153

Copyright © Wright Group/McGraw-Hill

Grade 6 Assessment Answers   **207**

LESSON 5·11 Mid-Year Assessment *continued*

The Science Club is selling packets of flower seeds. They spend $2 buying 40 packets of seeds at $0.05 each. They plan to charge $1 for each seed packet.

11. Complete the table at the right.

12. Use the grid at the right to graph the profit data from the table. Connect the points.

Number of seed packets sold (x)	Profit ($) (x − 2)
0	−2
2	0
4	2
8	6

Use the graph you made in Problem 12 to answer the following questions.

13. How many packets of seeds must the club sell to make a profit of $5?

___7___

14. What does the point (0, −2) on the graph represent? Sample answer: The club has a loss of $2 if no seed packets are sold.

15. Order from least to greatest.

a. $\frac{5}{8}, \frac{3}{1}, \frac{1}{5}, \frac{3}{1}, \frac{1}{8}$ $\frac{1}{8}, \frac{1}{5}, \frac{3}{8}, \frac{3}{5}, \frac{5}{8}$

b. $2.1, \frac{22}{10}, 2.01\frac{5}{2}, \frac{2}{11}$ $\frac{22}{11}, 2.01, 2.1, \frac{22}{10}, \frac{5}{2}$

16. Solve. Write each answer in simplest form.

a. $7 - 4\frac{3}{4} = \underline{\frac{9}{4}, \text{ or } 2\frac{1}{4}}$ b. $\frac{4}{9} + \frac{5}{6} = \underline{\frac{23}{18}, \text{ or } 1\frac{5}{18}}$

c. $3\frac{4}{5} - 2\frac{2}{3} = \underline{\frac{17}{15}, \text{ or } 1\frac{2}{15}}$ d. $3\frac{3}{4} * 4\frac{2}{5} = \underline{\frac{33}{2}, \text{ or } 16\frac{1}{2}}$

LESSON 5·11 Mid-Year Assessment *continued*

17. Complete the table. Simplify all fractions.

	Fraction	Decimal	Percent		Fraction	Decimal	Percent
a.	$\frac{11}{20}$	0.55	55%	e.	$\frac{7}{20}$	0.35	35%
b.	$\frac{1}{8}$	0.125	$12\frac{1}{2}$%	f.	$\frac{3}{8}$	0.375	37.5%
c.	$\frac{13}{52}$	0.25	25%	g.	$\frac{39}{50}$	0.78	78%
d.	$\frac{9}{200}$	0.045	$4\frac{1}{2}$%	h.	$\frac{4}{5}$	0.8	80%

Ms. McCarty's math students asked a total of 200 adults what time they left for work each weekday morning. The results of their survey appear in the table below.

18. Complete the table. Round measures to the nearest whole degree.

Departure Times for Work	Number of People	Percent of Total	Degree Measure of Sector
Before 6 A.M.	80	a. 40%	b. 144°
Between 6 A.M. and 7 A.M.	54	c. 27%	d. 97°
Between 7 A.M. and 8 A.M.	40	e. 20%	72°
After 8 A.M.	f. 26	13%	g. 47°
Total	200	100%	360°

19. Use a protractor to make a circle graph that displays the information above. Do not use the Percent Circle. Write a title for the graph.

20. Based on the survey results in Problem 18, about how many of 250 people would you expect to say that they left for work between 6 A.M. and 7 A.M.?

___67 or 68___ people

Morning Departure Times

LESSON 5·11 Mid-Year Assessment *continued*

21. Write an algebraic expression, using the suggested variable, to answer each of the following questions.

a. A tarantula spider has 8 legs. How many legs do *t* tarantulas have?   ___8t___ legs

b. Christina has *d* dollars. Her brother has $8 more than she has. How much money does Christina's brother have?   ___d + 8___ dollars

c. Bobbie's dog is *y* years old. How old was Bobbie's dog 8 years ago?   ___y − 8___ years old

22. Evaluate each expression when *x* = 3.

a. $9.2 * 10^x$ ___9,200___   b. $2^x * x$ ___24___

c. $10^{-x} * 5^x$ ___0.125___   d. $x^0 − 8$ ___−7___

23. Quadrilateral *PALE* is a parallelogram. Without using a protractor, find the degree measure of

a. ∠ALE.   ___110___°

b. ∠AEL.   ___30___°

c. ∠PEL.   ___70___°

24. Without using a protractor, find the degree measure of each numbered angle.

a. m∠1 = ___60___°

b. m∠2 = ___125___°

c. m∠3 = ___65___°

LESSON 5·11 Mid-Year Assessment *continued*

Part B

25. Graph the quadrilateral with the vertices given below. Label each vertex with the appropriate letter. Vertex *Y* has been plotted and labeled for you.

Y (1,2)   E (3,4)

A (6,0)   R (4,−2)

26. Without graphing the image, list the vertices of *Y′E′A′R′* resulting from translating each vertex of *YEAR* 1 unit left and 2 units up.

$Y'(\underline{0}, \underline{4})$; $E'(\underline{2}, \underline{6})$; $A'(\underline{5}, \underline{2})$; $R'(\underline{3}, \underline{0})$

27. Reflect *YEAR* (Problem 25) over the y-axis. Label the reflected image *Y″E″A″R″*.

28. This past summer, Vivian and her sister started a lawn-mowing and landscaping business. For four months, they recorded their income and expenses in the spreadsheet below. Use the spreadsheet to answer the questions that follow.

	A	B	C	D	E	F
1		May	June	July	August	Total
2	Income	$20.00	$65.50	$75.00	$55.75	$216.25
3	Expenses	$30.70	$5.15	$0.00	$5.85	$41.70

a. During which month did Vivian and her sister have the most expenses?   ___May___

b. In which cell does the business's July income appear?   ___D2___

c. Complete Column F of the spreadsheet above.

d. Write a spreadsheet formula you could use to find the mean income for the 4 months.

$\frac{B2 + C2 + D2 + E2}{4} = x$

---

208   Grade 6 Assessment Answers

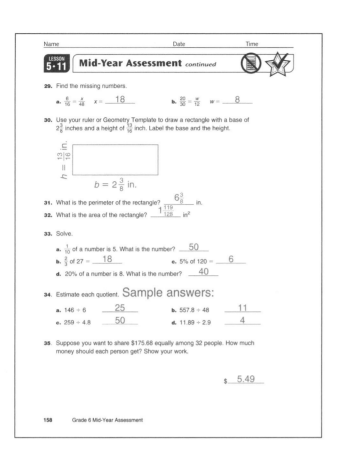

Name ___ **Date** ___ **Time** ___

LESSON 5·11 **Mid-Year Assessment** *continued*

29. Find the missing numbers.

  a. $\frac{6}{16} = \frac{x}{48}$ $x =$ __18__   b. $\frac{20}{30} = \frac{w}{12}$ $w =$ __8__

30. Use your ruler or Geometry Template to draw a rectangle with a base of $2\frac{3}{8}$ inches and a height of $\frac{13}{16}$ inch. Label the base and the height.

$h = \frac{13}{16}$ in.

$b = 2\frac{3}{8}$ in.

31. What is the perimeter of the rectangle? __$6\frac{3}{8}$__ in.
32. What is the area of the rectangle? __$1\frac{119}{128}$__ in²

33. Solve.

  a. $\frac{1}{10}$ of a number is 5. What is the number? __50__
  b. $\frac{2}{3}$ of 27 = __18__   c. 5% of 120 = __6__
  d. 20% of a number is 8. What is the number? __40__

34. Estimate each quotient. **Sample answers:**

  a. 146 ÷ 6 __25__   b. 557.8 ÷ 48 __11__
  c. 259 ÷ 4.8 __50__   d. 11.89 ÷ 2.9 __4__

35. Suppose you want to share $175.68 equally among 32 people. How much money should each person get? Show your work.

$ __5.49__

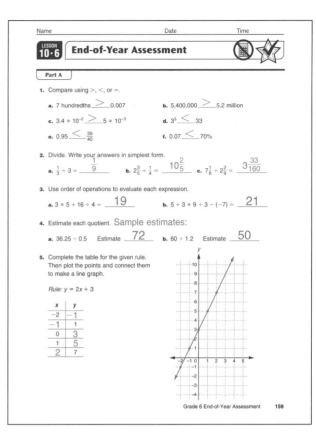

Name ___ **Date** ___ **Time** ___

LESSON 10·6 **End-of-Year Assessment**

Part A

1. Compare using >, <, or =.

  a. 7 hundredths __>__ 0.007   b. 5,400,000 __>__ 5.2 million
  c. $3.4 * 10^{-2}$ __>__ $5 * 10^{-3}$ d. 3^3 __<__ 33
  e. 0.95 __<__ $\frac{39}{40}$ f. 0.07 __<__ 70%

2. Divide. Write your answers in simplest form.

  a. $\frac{1}{3} \div 3 =$ __$\frac{1}{9}$__   b. $2\frac{3}{5} \div \frac{1}{4} =$ __$10\frac{2}{5}$__   c. $7\frac{1}{8} \div 2\frac{2}{9} =$ __$3\frac{33}{160}$__

3. Use order of operations to evaluate each expression.

  a. $3 * 5 + 16 \div 4 =$ __19__   b. $5 + 3 * 9 \div 3 - (-7) =$ __21__

4. Estimate each quotient. **Sample estimates:**

  a. 36.25 ÷ 0.5   Estimate __72__   b. 60 ÷ 1.2   Estimate __50__

5. Complete the table for the given rule. Then plot the points and connect them to make a line graph.

Rule: $y = 2x + 3$

x	y
−2	−1
−1	1
0	3
1	5
2	7

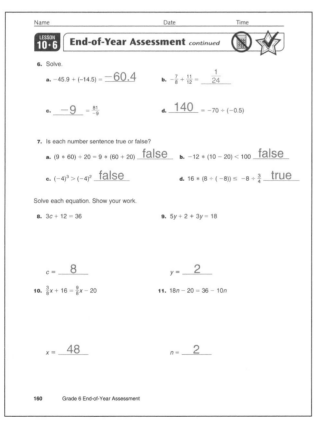

Name ___ **Date** ___ **Time** ___

LESSON 10·6 **End-of-Year Assessment** *continued*

6. Solve.

  a. $-45.9 + (-14.5) =$ __−60.4__   b. $-\frac{7}{8} + \frac{11}{12} =$ __$\frac{1}{24}$__

  c. __−9__ $= \frac{81}{-9}$ d. __140__ $= -70 \div (-0.5)$

7. Is each number sentence true or false?

  a. $(9 * 60) + 20 = 9 * (60 + 20)$ __false__   b. $-12 * (10 - 20) < 100$ __false__
  c. $(-4)^3 > (-4)^2$ __false__   d. $16 * (8 \div (-8)) \le -8 \div \frac{3}{4}$ __true__

Solve each equation. Show your work.

8. $3c + 12 = 36$

9. $5y + 2 + 3y = 18$

$c =$ __8__

$y =$ __2__

10. $\frac{3}{8}x + 16 = \frac{9}{8}x - 20$

11. $18n - 20 = 36 - 10n$

$x =$ __48__

$n =$ __2__

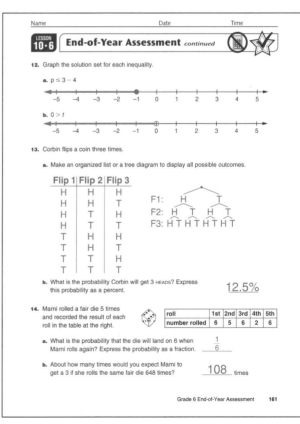

Name ___ **Date** ___ **Time** ___

LESSON 10·6 **End-of-Year Assessment** *continued*

12. Graph the solution set for each inequality.

  a. $p \le 3 - 4$

  b. $0 > t$

13. Corbin flips a coin three times.

  a. Make an organized list or a tree diagram to display all possible outcomes.

Flip 1	Flip 2	Flip 3
H	H	H
H	H	T
H	T	H
H	T	T
T	H	H
T	H	T
T	T	H
T	T	T

F1: H   T
F2: H T   H T
F3: H T H T H T H T

  b. What is the probability Corbin will get 3 HEADS? Express this probability as a percent. __12.5%__

14. Marni rolled a fair die 5 times and recorded the result of each roll in the table at the right.

roll	1st	2nd	3rd	4th	5th
number rolled	6	5	6	2	6

  a. What is the probability that the die will land on 6 when Marni rolls again? Express the probability as a fraction. __$\frac{1}{6}$__

  b. About how many times would you expect Marni to get a 3 if she rolls the same fair die 648 times? __108__ times

LESSON 10·6 **End-of-Year Assessment** *continued*

Solve each problem using any method.

15. Model railroad hobbyists can collect toy trains and equipment that are precise replicas of actual trains. The toy trains look exactly like the real trains they represent, only smaller.

There are four popular scales that appear in the table at the right.

Scale Name	Scale (inches) Model: Actual
N	$\frac{1}{160}$
HO	$\frac{1}{87}$
S	$\frac{1}{64}$
O	$\frac{1}{48}$

a. Each car on a full-size passenger train is 80 ft long. What is the length in inches of a model passenger car built on the S scale?

_____ **15** in.

b. An O-scale locomotive is 1.05 ft long. How long is the actual locomotive?

50.4 ft

c. A boxcar on an actual freight train is 40 ft long. A model boxcar is 3 in. long. In which scale was the model built?

N scale

16. A 16-oz box of *Sweety Pi* breakfast cereal costs $3.68. A 20-oz box costs $4.79. Which box is the better buy?

a. The _____ **16** -oz box of cereal is the better buy.

b. Explain how you determined which box is the better buy.

Sample answer: I divided $3.68 by 16 ounces to get $0.23 per ounce. Because $4.79 is very close to $4.80, I estimated before dividing: $4.80 ÷ 20 is $0.24. Based on my estimate, I concluded that the 20-ounce box costs more per ounce.

17. You have 45 coins. Five out of every 9 are HEADS up. How many coins are HEADS up? _____ **25** coins are HEADS up

---

 LESSON 10·6 **End-of-Year Assessment** *continued*

18. Triangles *MAY* and *JUL* are similar.

a. Measure the sides of each triangle to the nearest millimeter. Write the measurements next to the sides.

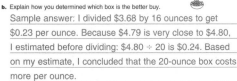

b. What is the size-change ratio between the two triangles? _____ **2:1**

19. Lines *p* and *q* are parallel and intersect the *x*- and *y*-axes to form similar right triangles.

a. What are the coordinates of point *G*?

(_____ **0** , _____ **12**)

b. Find the area of triangle *DEF*.

Area = _____ **24** units²

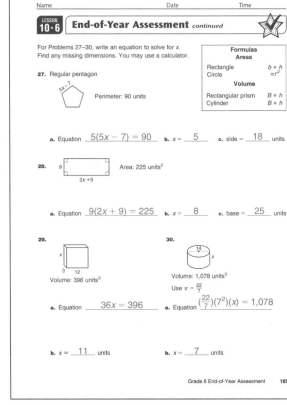

c. Use the Pythagorean theorem to find the length of $\overline{DF}$.

$\overline{DF}$ = _____ **10** units

Pythagorean theorem
$a^2 + b^2 = c^2$

d. Explain how you can use the dimensions of triangle *DEF* to find the perimeter of triangle *GER*.

Sample answer: Because triangles *DEF* and *GER* are similar, I used a proportion to find the length of $\overline{GR}$; $\frac{9}{6} = \frac{x}{10}$; x = 15. So, the perimeter of triangle *GER* equals 9 + 12 + 15 = 36 units.

LESSON 10·6 **End-of-Year Assessment** *continued*

20. Write each number as a percent.

a. 0.3 **30%** **b.** 0.021 **2.1%** **c.** 1.5 **150%** **d.** 0.09 **9%**

21. Complete the table. Write each fraction in simplest form.

	Fraction	Decimal	Percent
a.	$\frac{7}{8}$	0.875	87.5%
b.	$\frac{18}{25}$	0.72	72%
c.	$\frac{3}{50}$	0.06	6%
d.	$\frac{1}{200}$	0.005	0.5%

Solve Problems 22–26 using any method. Show your work. Sample work shown.

22. Find 56% of 75.
75 * 0.56

56% of 75 is _____ **42** .

23. What percent of 25 is 17?
25x = 17
$x = \frac{17}{25} = \frac{68}{100}$
17 is _____ **68** % of 25.

24. 120 is 15% of what number?
$\frac{15}{100}x = 120$
$x = \frac{120}{1} * \frac{100}{15}$
x = 800
120 is 15% of _____ **800** .

25. Find 150% of 90.
90 * 1.5
150% of 90 is _____ **135** .

26. Software for a personal digital assistant (PDA) that regularly sells for $60 is on sale for 15% off. Find the sale price.

Sale price _____ **$51**

LESSON 10·6 **End-of-Year Assessment** *continued*

For Problems 27–30, write an equation to solve for *x*. Find any missing dimensions. You may use a calculator.

Formulas	
Areas	
Rectangle	$b * h$
Circle	πr^2
Volume	
Rectangular prism	$B * h$
Cylinder	$B * h$

27. Regular pentagon

Perimeter: 90 units

a. Equation _____ **5(5x − 7) = 90** **b.** *x* = _____ **5** **c.** side = _____ **18** units

28. Area: 225 units²

a. Equation _____ **9(2x + 9) = 225** **b.** *x* = _____ **8** **c.** base = _____ **25** units

29. Volume: 396 units³

a. Equation _____ **36x = 396**

b. *x* = _____ **11** units

30. Volume: 1,078 units³
Use $\pi = \frac{22}{7}$

a. Equation _____ $\left(\frac{22}{7}\right)(7^2)(x) = 1,078$

b. *x* = _____ **7** units

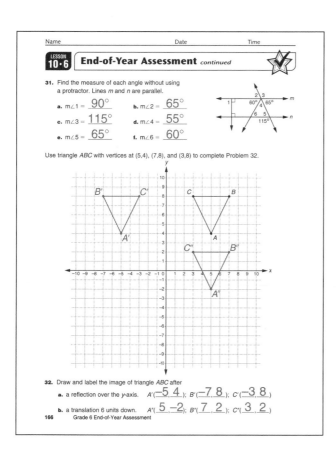

LESSON 10·6 **End-of-Year Assessment** *continued*

31. Find the measure of each angle without using a protractor. Lines *m* and *n* are parallel.

a. m∠1 = __90°__   **b.** m∠2 = __65°__

c. m∠3 = __115°__   **d.** m∠4 = __55°__

e. m∠5 = __65°__   **f.** m∠6 = __60°__

Use triangle *ABC* with vertices at (5,4), (7,8), and (3,8) to complete Problem 32.

32. Draw and label the image of triangle *ABC* after

a. a reflection over the *y*-axis. A'(__-5, 4__); B'(__-7, 8__); C'(__-3, 8__)

b. a translation 6 units down. A''(__5, -2__); B''(__7, 2__); C''(__3, 2__)

166   Grade 6 End-of-Year Assessment

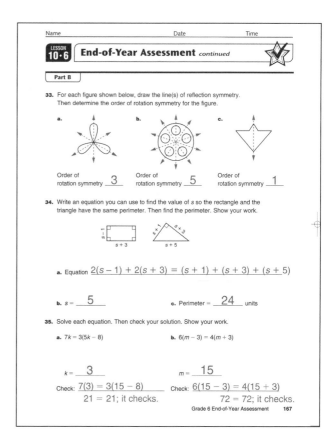

LESSON 10·6 **End-of-Year Assessment** *continued*

Part B

33. For each figure shown below, draw the line(s) of reflection symmetry. Then determine the order of rotation symmetry for the figure.

a.   Order of rotation symmetry __3__

b.   Order of rotation symmetry __5__

c.   Order of rotation symmetry __1__

34. Write an equation you can use to find the value of *s* so the rectangle and the triangle have the same perimeter. Then find the perimeter. Show your work.

a. Equation $2(s - 1) + 2(s + 3) = (s + 1) + (s + 3) + (s + 5)$

b. s = __5__   **c.** Perimeter = __24__ units

35. Solve each equation. Then check your solution. Show your work.

a. $7k = 3(5k - 8)$ **b.** $6(m - 3) = 4(m + 3)$

k = __3__ m = __15__

Check: $7(3) = 3(15 - 8)$ Check: $6(15 - 3) = 4(15 + 3)$
        $21 = 21$; it checks. $72 = 72$; it checks.

Grade 6 End-of-Year Assessment   167